BACH FLOWER REMEDIES:

HUMOR TO REMEMBER THEM
or . . . First, Get the Elephant Off Your Foot

"Your book is certainly novel in its humorous approach to the subject of Bach Flower Remedies. It should help, through the cartoon system, to perhaps enhance one's ability to identify and recognize the mental aspect of each remedy. We have always considered that healing can be better conveyed through the virtues of joy and love, to help instill faith and hope in those who have been drawn into the whirlpool of mental suffering. Your book should help to bring this uplifting of attitudes into being."

--- John Ramsell, Trustee and Curator
The Dr. Edward Bach Centre; England

First, Get the Elephant Off Your Foot
See Vervain, Page 96,
as you happily get your own life in perspective.

BACH FLOWER REMEDIES:

HUMOR TO REMEMBER THEM

or . . . First,
Get the Elephant Off Your Foot

by
Joyce Petrak, D.C.H.

- John R. Stowe

Illustrated by: Ben Delphia
David B. Roth
John R. Stowe

Important Message

Neither author or publishers are medical doctors and make no claims to the medical effectiveness of Bach Flower Remedies. The enclosed is for educational purposes only. All stories are anecdotal and not substantiated by clinical proof. The author does not answer medical questions. Proper care by a certified medical doctor should be sought immediately if there is sufficient cause to use a physician. This book is not for diagnosing, treating or prescribing for any illness.

Also by Joyce Petrak, DCH:

"Angels, Guides & Other Spirits"

Incredible events

from the unseen world around us

as told by a SPIRIT RELEASE THERAPIST.

* * *

Joyce Petrak, DCH
Curry-Peterson Press
238 Chahyga Circle
Loudon, TN 37774

ISBN: 0-9633177-3-3

DEDICATION

To the constant help and guidance of Holy Spirit
in my life . . . sometimes, not always gently.

To the beautiful inspiration received from the
writings and works of Dr. Edward Bach.
We hope he gets a laugh from the book.

To my many teachers, clients, students and friends
from whom I have learned so much.

To my best friend and supportive spouse, Bob.
Last, but never least.

EDWARD BACH M.D., Physician, Bacteriologist
Discoverer of the Healing Essence in Flowers
(Courtesy of the Bach Centre)

Table of Contents

INTRODUCTION

No one reads introductions. But, in case you do, may I introduce myself. I'm Joyce Petrak and I'm delighted to meet you in the pages of this book. It was originally written for my students who were struggling to distinguish between the 38 Bach Remedies. Since I feel "Laughter is the best medicine" and visual aids greatly assist in remembering, this book evolved. I'm extremely pleased that so many all over the U.S. and Canada have found it helpful. I always enjoy hearing from readers.

I hope this book is helpful to you. The Remedies truly are miracles of grace and I pray that you will love, understand and utilize them more each year. First, for yourself . . . that your personality may develop and a richer loving-ness and happier vitality will emerge. You deserve it! Blessings, also for all those whom you meet and touch and care for that they, too, will be enlightened . . . and thus be healed.

May our Creator continuously brighten your days with His wonderful spiritual gifts . . . the flowers.

What Are Bach Flower Remedies?

Dr. Bach believed that the ills of the heart and the spirit must be the focus of a healer's attention. He discovered a **medical connection between feelings and actual physical illness.**

Using Homeopathic principles, he developed herbal remedies from 38 non-poisonous plants. From 4 to 6 Remedies are usually in a person's formula. They are taken in the form of four drops, four times a day. In "Heal Thyself," Dr. Bach wrote: "Behind all disease lie our fears, our anxieties, our greed, our likes and dislikes. Let us seek those out and heal them, and with the healing will go the disease from which we suffer."

Dr. Bach offered no scientific explanation for the Remedies but **thousands of successful case histories** have convinced many practitioners of their great value. Herbert Fill, M.D., Psychiatrist, former NY Commissioner of Mental Health, said, "The Remedies are **extremely sophisticated** in their action. They are **unusually gentle** and yet profoundly potent in their effect on balancing out the body's subtle energy fields. I use them almost exclusively instead of tranquilizers and psychotropes and get very good results. In many cases they alleviate the problems where all else has failed."

There is no such thing as "Take a pill and we are cured." As Dr. Bach found, **"Bodily ills are only symptoms."** The Remedies do not attack disease, but, like beautiful music, flood our natures with the virtues we need. As our Higher Natures prevail, disease melts like snow in the sunshine.

The Flower Remedies **do not interfere** with any other healing methods, even drugs. Since they feed our Spiritual Nature, they are very compatible with wholesome food and supplements which are needed to nourish our Physical Nature.

RESCUE, a combination of five Remedies, is the most famous and is used for emergencies, crisis, or such stress as accidents, near accidents, stage or interview fright, a medical or dental procedure, etc.

WHAT IS RESCUE?!!

For emergencies large and small, thousands of us would not be without **Rescue.** We carry it in purse or pocket, never knowing when someone . . . or ourselves . . . will have a traumatic experience. Now that doesn't mean we are out looking for unfortunate events - only that we want to be prepared IF one occurs. Dispensing drops from this one ounce bottle of seeming miracles, either internally or externally, has relieved millions of large and small traumas.

Since 1930, when Dr. Bach researched the combination of Remedies which he called **Rescue,** it has relieved stresses, pain, fears, shock, sorrow and any other imaginable negative emotion. Many claim it has saved lives.

Rescue is not another Remedy but a combination of five: **Clematis** for clear thinking needed in an emergency (or to bring a person back to consciousness); **Impatiens** to calm a person down. (Dr. Bach felt **Impatiens** should always be used with pain.) **Rock Rose** is for terror or panic; **Cherry Plum** helps a person stay in control in case of fright, hysteria, shock or immobility; **Star of Bethlehem** neutralizes any fright or trauma.

Rescue should not take the place of medical attention but can do much to alleviate stress and nervousness until help arrives. Although everyone using Bach Remedies has some great **Rescue** stories, there have never been clinical studies done which leaves it in a medical no-man's-land. However, many doctors, dentists, chiropractors, massage and physical therapists, as well as hypno-therapists and many other kinds of therapists, have used it for years with excellent results.

Rescue should normally be used only for temporary situations. Some people use only **Rescue.** They are very crisis conscious—and we're glad they have **Rescue** to help—but they should be getting Remedies for their own personality type for long-range progress with deep seated emotions and weaknesses. None of us is perfect and we should be aware that there are 38 different Remedies to help us.

When we start working on ourselves and our growth, it takes time. With **Rescue,** however, immediate results are usually seen. Four drops are taken internally and/or externally when a challenge develops. In a serious crisis, the drops can be given every two minutes until the person is stabilized. There are no side effects. As a situation becomes less serious, the drops can be given (or taken) every 15, 30 or 60 minutes. Many people give the drops to themselves when they feel anxious or nervous.

A person giving **Rescue** to someone else should usually take the drops also, as it is important for a caregiver to remain calm and clear minded when helping someone.

For a more in-depth understanding of **Rescue,** see page 112.

AT A GLANCE REFERENCE TO THE BACH REMEDIES

1. **Agrimony.** Those who suffer considerable inner torture which they try to dissemble behind a facade of cheerfulness.

2. **Aspen.** Apprehension and foreboding. Fears of unknown origin.

3. **Beech.** Critical and intolerant of others. Arrogant.

4. **Centaury.** Weakness of will; those who let themselves be exploited or imposed upon - become subservient; difficulty in saying 'no.' Human doormat.

5. **Cerato.** Those who doubt their own judgment, seeks advice of others. Often influenced and misguided.

6. **Cherry Plum.** Fear of mental collapse/desperation/loss of control and fear of causing harm. Vicious rages.

7. **Chestnut Bud.** Refusal to learn by experience; continually repeating the same mistakes.

8. **Chicory.** The over-possessive, demands respect or attention (selfishness), likes others to conform to their standards. Makes martyr of oneself, self-pity.

9. **Clematis.** Indifferent, inattentive, dreamy, absent-minded. Mental escapist from reality.

10. **Crab Apple.** Cleanser. Feels unclean or ashamed of ailments. Self-disgust/hatred. For cleaning out toxins.

11. **Elm.** For temporary feelings of inadequacy; overwhelmed by responsibilities.

12. **Gentian.** Despondent. Easily discouraged and dejected, self doubt.

13. **Gorse.** Extreme hopelessness - pessimist - 'Oh, what's the use.'

14. **Heather.** People who are obsessed with own troubles and experiences. Talkative 'bores' - poor listeners.

15. **Holly.** For those who are jealous, envious, revengeful and suspicious. For those who hate.

16. **Honeysuckle.** For those with nostalgia and who constantly dwell in the past. Homesickness.

17. **Hornbeam.** 'Monday morning' feeling but once started, task is usually fulfilled. Procrastination.

18. **Impatiens.** Impatience, irritability.

19. **Larch.** Despondency due to lack of self-confidence; expectation of failure, so fails to make the attempt. Feels inferior though has the ability.

20. **Mimulus.** Fear of known things. Shyness, timidity.

21. **Mustard.** Deep gloom like an overshadowing dark cloud that descends for no known reason which can lift just as suddenly. Melancholy.

22. **Oak.** Brave determined types, struggles on against adversity despite setbacks. Plodders.

23. **Olive.** Extreme tiredness - drained of energy - everything an effort.

24. **Pine.** Feelings of guilt. May blame self for other's mistakes. Always feel they should do better.

25. **Red Chestnut.** Excessive fear and over caring for others especially those held dear.

26. **Rock Rose.** Terror, extreme fear or panic.

27. **Rock Water.** For those who are hard on themselves - often overwork. Rigid minded, self denying.

28. **Scleranthus.** Uncertainty/indecision/vacillation. Fluctuating moods.

29. **Star of Bethlehem.** For all the effects of serious news, or fright following an accident, etc. Any of life's traumas.

30. **Sweet Chestnut.** Anguish of those who have reached the limit of endurance - only oblivion left.

31. **Vervain.** Over-enthusiasm, over-effort; straining. Fanatical and highly-strung. Incensed by injustices.

32. **Vine.** Dominating/inflexible/ambitious/tyrannical. Loves power. Can make good leaders.

33. **Walnut.** Protection remedy from powerful influences. Helps adjustment to any transition or change, e.g. puberty, menopause, divorce, new surroundings, job.

34. **Water Violet.** Proud, reserved, sedate types, sometimes 'superior.' Little emotional involvement but reliable/dependable.

35. **White Chestnut.** Persistent unwanted thoughts. Preoccupation with some worry or episode. Mental arguments.

36. **Wild Oat.** Helps determine one's intended path in life.

37. **Wild Rose.** Resignation, apathy. Drifters who accept their lot, making little effort for improvement - lack ambition.

38. **Willow.** Resentment and bitterness with 'not fair' and 'poor me' attitude.

39. **RESCUE REMEDY** - a combination of Cherry Plum, Clematis, Impatiens, Rock Rose, Star of Bethlehem. All purpose emergency composite for causes of fright, anguish, panic, emotional upsets, 'stage fright,' examinations, going to the dentist, etc.

Who Was Dr. Bach?

What rejoicing there must have been in the Bach household when Edward finally got enough courage to tell his father he wanted to go to medical school. When he had finished school at 16, the dutiful son had gone to work at his father's brass factory in Birmingham, England.

He worked at the lathes in various departments but so disliked the indoors, noise and regular hours that his father sent him out to do commercial sales. He had been delicate since birth but was very idealistic, highly intuitive and had strong powers of concentration.

However, these gifts were of little use in the commercial world. It wasn't that he didn't get any orders. It was just that he loved people so much he gave them a very good deal . . . so good that his father couldn't fill the orders and make a profit.

After three years, the father was probably somewhat distraught about his oldest child who was obviously not going to be a captain of industry. Sending him to medical school in 1906, at the age of 20, was no doubt a festive occasion for the whole family.

Edward Bach had grown up with a great love for people and for nature. He was deeply disturbed whenever he saw a person or animal suffering. This developed into his aspiration to be a healer although, at times, he felt he should join the ministry because Jesus was a great healer and he felt this should be a work of the church.

IN LONDON

Although he disliked the noise and traffic of London, he rarely left because he was afraid the call of Nature would be so strong he wouldn't want to return. He didn't want to be distracted from his goal of finding ways to ease the pains of man.

His health was not too good but he worked ceaselessly at his studies, and reading anything else he could find on healing. He also studied patients intently and realized that the same medication would not heal everyone with a particular illness. He became aware that people with the same temperament would often respond to the same remedy. He early understood that "the personality of the individual is of even more importance than the body in the treatment of his disease."

He felt that the frequent medical failures were because doctors had little time to study their patients. They concentrated so much on the physical body, they did not appreciate that each individual was different. Very early he understood that the disease should not be the focus of attention.

GRAVE ILLNESS

Dr. Bach was graduated in 1912 at the age of 25. He worked at a hospital but also spent many hours at research. During World War I, in 1914, he was in charge of over 400 wounded in addition to doing research. As months of intense work continued, he would frequently feel ill and faint at his laboratory bench.

In July 1917 he had a severe hemorrhage and became unconscious. An operation was performed but, when he awoke, he was told the disease would likely spread and, at most, he had three months to live. There was so much he wanted to do but he was in agony of mind as well as body. Finally, he decided to make use of what little time he had, and returned to the hospital laboratory. He became so immersed in his experiments that he paid no attention to time. He knew he was growing stronger, however. At the end of three months, he astonished doctors by being in good health. Dr. Bach then understood that an absorbing interest and definite purpose in life can determine a person's health and happiness.

SUCCESSFUL RESEARCH

In 1918 there was a flu outbreak which killed thousands until Dr. Bach's new vaccine was used. It saved many lives and his work started to be noticed.

He practiced conventional medicine until 1919 when he went to the London Homeopathic Hospital as pathologist and bacteriologist. Reading the writings of Hahnemann, the founder of Homeopathy, he was excited that someone else understood, "Treat the patient and not the disease."

Bach felt that by combining Hahnemann's discoveries with his own, he could extend and improve on both. He worked on preparing vaccines from intestinal organisms according to homeopathic methods. He had great success and was considered a genius and "second Hahnemann" by his peers. His research continued, however, because he wanted to replace intestinal bacteria with herbs and plants.

THE FIRST REMEDIES

This led him to the Wales countryside. Always intense and anxious, he first found the Impatiens flower. With his great intuition, he knew it would help him to be calmer and more relaxed. Later, he may have developed a fear because, when he tasted a **Mimulus** flower, he was no longer fearful. Another flower he found, which was to become the third Remedy, was the lovely **Clematis**. This helped him to gather his thoughts and concentrate on his work with a clear mind.

He was very excited with his findings and soon decided that the flowers of the field were now to be the focus of his work. He was making excellent money at this point and had many devoted patients, and close friends and colleagues. You can imagine the number of incredulous comments he received when he announced he was leaving his practice. "You're going to do what?" and "You're leaving all this to go and look for wild flowers?" His friends worried about his sanity.

He was not to be dissuaded, however, and in 1930, at the age of 43, he left London. He received some money from the sale of his lab equipment but he actually had relatively little . . . and no definite plans. He considered healing a divine art and, from the time he left London, he rarely charged a fee. He often did without things but, somehow, gifts and contributions resulted in his always managing.

MORE REMEDIES

He felt an instant body reaction if he held a petal or flower in his palm or on his tongue. Some gave him strength and energy of body and mind; others gave him pains, fevers, rashes and even vomiting. He said his body was better equipped than any laboratory.

In this way, he discovered the dew of the flower contained the healing properties. This is when he started to potentize stock water by putting the flowers in a bowl of spring water on a sunny day.

He wrote the inspiring book, "Heal Thyself," and wandered the fields for hundreds of miles, finding more Remedies. Dr. Bach also had the gift of healing and, at times, could simply put his hand on someone and they would be healed. However, he didn't know how to help other people learn this. But he could teach them how to use the flowers to heal.

THE TOUGH ONES

Although he was usually having remarkable results with the 12 Remedies he had discovered, he knew there were more to be found for the states of mind which were deeper and more persistent.

After he had 19 Remedies, he looked for a permanent dwelling and rented Mount Vernon in the village of Sotwell. Today, this is still world headquarters for the Bach Centre although it has been enlarged and plumbing added (Dr. Bach had no indoor plumbing).

He settled down to work, seeing many patients and answering heavy correspondence from all over the world. It was at this point he began training three lay workers in all aspects of his work. Reports from them, and from laity and professionals everywhere the Remedies traveled, were excellent and he was delighted. His goal seemed to be close but he knew there were still more Remedies to be discovered.

THE FINAL 19

Knowledge of the second 19 Remedies came to him far differently. For some time before the discovery of each, he suffered the state of mind for which a Remedy was needed. He had terrible intense mental agonies, often accompanied with severe physical sickness. At times he could not stand or sit comfortably and could not rest. Still he dragged himself out, going by bicycle or car if he was too sick to walk. Only when he found the correct flower or flowering tree, and potentized it, could he be free from the torture. Once he was completely covered with a poisonous rash which burned and irritated him constantly. For some weeks his legs were ulcerated and raw. Another time his hair fell out and he almost lost his sight. Once he became exhausted from a severe hemorrhage, which did not stop until he found the remedy for the mental state he was passing through.

While the year 1935 was very hard on him, he was a happy, joyful person when well. He laughed and joked with staff and townspeople. Having discovered 38 Remedies, he now felt it was time to let the world know about them. He and his staff planned some lectures and he gave the first one on his 50th birthday, September 24, 1936.

Toward the end of October, however, he lost his strength and had to stay in bed. He continued to instruct his staff and made light of his condition. He rallied briefly but on November 27, 1936, he died in his sleep.

Why so young? Well, simply, his work was finished. He did not fear death and believed he would continue working on another sphere. To the world, to us, he left a magnificent legacy: an understanding that the Creator has provided us with the flowers of the fields to help suffering mankind into a bright and happy future.

WHO NEEDS THIS STUFF??

The most important thing to know about Bach Flower Remedies is

THEY WORK!!

For milleniums skeptical humans have dismissed the discoveries of advanced souls. "It won't work," has greeted the Bells, Edisons and thousands of other inventors and researchers who tried to improve upon existing conditions.

Their zeal for progress could be matched by Edward Bach, M.D., who wanted "simply" to cure the sufferings of mankind. A brilliant researcher, as well as a great humanitarian, Bach early discovered that the personality, attitude and present outlook of a patient had much to do with his being cured or remaining sick.

Now Hippocrates knew this in 400 B.C. and modern researchers frequently tell us this. And yet, somehow, the medical profession (as well as most patients) keep looking for the drug (or vitamin) that will be a quick cure for each ailment that comes along.

"If you focus only on the physical goal, you are, ultimately, always going to fail. If you focus on learning how to live and love, then you can really accomplish something," according to surgeon Bernie S. Siegel.[1]

Dr. Bach understood all this and also that the Creator had provided simple, natural means for healing that could be used by any caring person. Thus he was led to certain wild flowers that could flood the soul with a beautiful, positive attitude and diseases then "melted like snow in the sunshine."

DISEASES WOULD THEN MELT LIKE SNOW IN THE SUNSHINE

How powerful! How simple! Yet, even Bach students often forget this when in pain or ill health. "Forget what illnesses you have!" they need.to be reminded. What is your mental condition? Are you feeling overwhelmed? (**Elm**); Guilty (**Pine**); Exhausted? (**Olive**); Resentful? (**Willow**) and so on.

> Take care of the most important <u>thing</u> first.
> Get your MA (mental attitude) into a loving,
> positive, grateful, forgiving mode. FIRST!

Love powerfully stimulates the immune system. To quote Dr. Siegel again, ". . . the state of mind changes the state of the body by working through the central nervous system, the endocrine system, the

---

1. Siegel, Bernie S., *Love, Medicine and Miracles,* Harper and Row.

immune system. Peace of mind sends the body a 'live' message, while depression, fear, and unresolved conflict give it a 'die' message."[2]

Many think of Bach's **Rescue** Remedy in a crisis of fear, anguish or pain. Millions have no doubt been helped by **Rescue**. But Dr. Bach discovered 38 different Remedies before his demise in 1936. They all can have important uses for us. We need to stop thinking of only crisis care. We need to think in terms of long-term help for ourselves and others since many illnesses take years before they manifest physically.

By really taking a good look at ourselves, we can discover our negative emotions. They may have been deep at a cellular level for a long time but we have not been conscious of them. It takes some patience and understanding to realize that it will take awhile to dissolve deep-seated feelings and beliefs.

A formula mixture lasts about 2½ weeks if taken four drops four times a day. Usually, the same exact formula is not taken for more than two bottles. By then, some Remedies are no longer needed. However, single Remedies that are needed for deep personality characteristics, like Impatiens or Vervain (intense, hard-driving), require a long time to modify if the person is in the negative mode of these traits.

When people say that Bach's "medicine" doesn't work, usually they have not been taking them regularly (four drops, four times a day is recommended) or long enough. Also, I find that, because they work so subtly, a person's whole life may be changing but this hasn't been related to the Remedies.

Sometimes the situation may seem to get worse as there is a "healing crisis" to make a person aware that other measures need to be taken. For instance, if a person takes **Rescue** several times for a leg pain and the pain increases, it may mean that a doctor is required. Mental or emotional pain could indicate that a therapist is needed if the situation worsens. Like a wound which needs cleaning out, sometimes our inner pain must be discussed with an understanding person so that it can be shared and put into a new perspective.

Fortunately, pain does make mankind think and it is often the only way to get attention to help him/her realize something needs to be done. Many are very adept at covering up inner feelings.

There is a possibility that the formula was incorrect but I rarely find that it was so bad that there were no good effects. Most practitioners find that it is best to use four or less different Remedies in

2. Ibid. Page 3.

a person's formula. Sometimes we use five if they can work synergistically. For instance, a person may need **Olive** for exhaustion but also would be helped to sleep better by having **White Chestnut** so the mind could stop going around and around at night.

Destroying the Remedies by leaving them in extremely high temperatures might be another reason why they seemed not to work. Also, some of us believe that touching the glass pipette to the mouth, and getting some saliva acids, could perhaps destroy the formula. *(See Page 32 for other explanations.)*

BUT THE REMEDIES DO WORK!!

For over 60 years now, the enlightened who have used Dr. Bach's formulas have found them to be always helpful, frequently life saving.

We need to increase the understanding that we should not wait for a crisis to start the Remedies. Indeed, prevention of illnesses is always preferable. By working with our faults, negativities and fears, we slowly grow mentally, physically and spiritually.

Like peeling away the thin sheets of an onion, we learn more about ourselves as we continue with the Remedies. For instance, at first we might disclaim that we have any jealousy in us. After using the Remedies for awhile, we might see that **Holly** (for jealousy, envy, hatred, or any absence of love) could be very beneficial for us. In this way, we continue to reach down into our psyche and gently dissolve all that separates us from Divine Love.

There is one primary error which man can make, and that is action against Unity; this originates in self-centeredness .. .

The real primary diseases of man are such defects as pride, cruelty, hate, self-centeredness, ignorance, instability and greed; and each of these, if considered, will be found to be adverse to Unity.

--Edward Bach, M.D., *Heal Thyself*

Depression, Despair and Bach Remedies

While any negative state can cause depression, there are specific Bach Remedies addressing this condition. They go from mild depression to the blackest of despair. It is not always easy to decide just which Remedy to use and, indeed, there are times when more than one needs to be used for the problem.

For instance, an **Oak** personality, who is a heavy burden bearer, never gives up and is always plodding along, may be in mild or deep depression. The person receives **Oak** to make him/her more flexible and then, perhaps, **Gentian** because things have gone wrong and he/she is really discouraged and mildly depressed.

It will be helpful to understand the various states of mind for dealing with depressions.

MILD STATES

Feeling overwhelmed by responsibility and inadequate for the tasks ahead can cause depression and mental exhaustion. If the people to whom this happens are basically capable and self-assured, Remedy **Elm** puts them into the positive again. It helps them as efficient leaders and decision makers, whether it be head of a household, business or country.

A **Gentian** type of person can also be depressed when things go wrong or there are setbacks. Basically, they believe in themselves, but sometimes get so low they forget that their negative attitude is attracting the depressing conditions. With the **Gentian** Remedy, they surge ahead with renewed determination and the understanding that there can be no failure, only lessons to be learned.

A **Larch** person is somewhat opposite as they have little self-confidence or belief in themselves. Feeling sure they will fail, they make little effort until **Larch** pulls them out of their depression.

Fears diminish as they refuse to be discouraged by temporary results and determine to try again. It's excellent before exams.

MEDIUM DEPRESSION

If there has been trauma (or this is the first time a person has received Remedies), **Star of Bethlehem** is important. It will neutralize any shocks the person has received, presently or anytime in their life. Dr. Bach called it "the comforter and soother of pains and sorrows." It may be the most important Remedy in **Rescue** and will work synergistically with any other Remedy.

If there is pain, we also look to see what guilt people have. Often with over-conscientious people, we find they are depressed from blaming themselves for everything that goes wrong, even the mistakes of others. **Pine** can be used to relieve these people of judging themselves as they aim to be more fair and balanced.

Sometimes confused with **Pine, Crab Apple** is more of a self-hatred as they are disgusted with something they have said or done. It is also a general cleanser for body as well as mind, as it can help with pollution and internal or external toxins.

Resentment, a "things aren't fair" attitude, can cause an irritable wet blanket until **Willow** is taken. It provides the magic drops which help regain a sense of humor and restores optimism and balance.

The worst of these states is **Gorse,** which is a hopelessness and depression from feeling nothing more can be done. It is a relatively passive state and, if it becomes pure apathy, **Wild Rose** needs to be added. In most cases, a **Gorse** type can usually be persuaded to try various suggestions even though the heart isn't in it.

DEEP DEPRESSION, DESPAIR

For no known reason, a big, gloomy cloud of depression lights on a person who is then barely able to function. After an hour, a day, or maybe a few days, the dark cloud lifts just as suddenly.

Mustard is the Remedy which will assist the despairing out of this sad state from an unknown cause. Inner serenity, peace and joy return.

In the worst state, there is total depression as the sufferer feels horrible mental anguish. This can happen in a bereavement or loss (such as a job loss), as they see no hope and feel no peace. The gentle healing of **Sweet Chestnut** causes them to regain control of their emotions and, despite their grief, to call on higher guidance and trust in the answer. Miracles can then be seen.

Sweet Chestnut is a fairly passive state as opposed to **Cherry Plum** where the person is out of control and ready to do something desperate. Suicide, murder or other violent impulses all need **Cherry Plum.** Since the problem can be rage or hysteria, it is not usually considered as depression, a more deeply introverted state where a person hardly feels like moving.

Some depressions have serious causes, others can be as simple as the weather. When winter seems to be forever, and the days are still too dark and short, many people feel irritable and depressed. It is then that they need the Remedies to "flood the soul with sunshine."

Which ones? See what the rest of the mental attitude is. There is something for everyone.

ADDICTIONS

For people trying to improve their health and/or well-being, an addiction to sugar, caffeine and/or smoking can prove to be a great stumbling block. Food addiction, alcoholism and drug abuse can be even more serious. If a person is really willing to stop a habit, Dr. Bach's flowers are a tremendous reinforcement.

Bach Remedies can be very helpful but a person usually has to be willing to do other things also. Visualization, deep breathing exercises, certain vitamin and detoxifying supplements or herbs, lots of good water and fasting can be most beneficial. Physical exercise and a temporary change in eating habits can also aid a person while they are working to change the computer in their head that says they need an offending substance.

While addictions are not mentioned in most of the Bach literature, we have had good luck giving a person a formula of **Rescue** plus **Chicory** and **Walnut**. The **Rescue** has **Impatiens** to keep them patient with themselves; **Clematis** for clear thinking and **Cherry Plum** so they don't go out of control and return to their addiction.

The **Rock Rose** is for the terror some feel at the thought of trying to change and **Star of Bethlehem** for the emotional trauma they feel. The **Chicory** is normally for selfish, demanding people who are full of self-pity. A person trying to get over an addiction may normally be just the opposite of this state. However, while kicking the habit, they might do a "poor little me" scene very easily. **Chicory** is to keep someone from feeling sorry for self.

Walnut is for any change in life and freeing oneself from a destructive habit is certainly a big change. In addition, **Larch** (for someone doubtful about sticking with their resolve) can aid in giving self-confidence. Another Remedy, **Chestnut Bud,** which is for those who continue to make the same mistakes in life, would especially help anyone who has tried to quit before and failed.

Again, it is important to remember that each person must be considered individually. What habit are you trying to change? Bach can be extremely helpful.

What To Do For Pain

If you are in pain, and know it is not something that requires a doctor's attention, you may find relief in Bach Flower Remedies. If it is a sudden, sharp pain, such as from a burn, deep scratch or insect bite, many would run for the **Rescue** Creme or liquid. It is miraculous in its quick acting effect.

If the pain is of a more enduring kind, however, it is important to remember that the Remedy needed ALWAYS depends on the person's mental state at the time. In deciding which of the 38 Remedies to use, the illness or disease itself is not considered. Each person is treated as an individual.

If a person is in such agony that they feel they are going out of their mind, **Cherry Plum** would be the right one. It's for anyone who feels out of control, possibly about to do something desperate.

IMPATIENT, TENSE

Dr. Bach said that **Impatiens** is usually called for with pain. This is because pain can result from mental tension which will tighten up muscles and cause many disorders. The person may be impatient, nervous and/or irritable and any noise, frustration, or even touching the affected area, can cause more tension and pain. (**Impatiens** is in **Rescue**, as is **Cherry Plum**.)

In "Heal Your Body," Louise Hay attributes pain to guilt and the consequent need to be punished. Pain may not always come from guilt but we have found it true often enough that we always consider **Pine** (for guilt) when there is pain.

Another frequent pain possibility is the tension caused by a person mentally hard against someone. **Willow** is the Remedy for resentment, bitterness, or an "I don't deserve this type of treatment" attitude. **Rock Water** is for the rigid, stubborn type who may be tense because of being so hard on self or because unforgiveness of others is too difficult.

Of course, if daily headaches come from the caffeine in coffee or pop (a frequent cause), you may need **Chicory** to help you get away from your addiction. **Chicory** is also helpful if a person has acquired pain so others will feel sorry for him/her. As you can see, your pain is a very individual situation. It's because you are unique.

Fears

Five different types of fears were listed by Dr. Bach. The first two, and the most severe types, are in **Rescue.** *They are* **Cherry Plum** *and* **Rock Rose.** *You may read about the individual ones on their own page, but this will give brief distinctions.*

Cherry Plum is a fear of losing control . . . this can be of thoughts or actions. This could be as severe as a murderous or suicidal feeling. It could be rage or hysteria. It could also be a person's fear that they might do something impulsive, that they know is wrong, and wouldn't do under ordinary circumstances.

Rock Rose is for stark terror . . . extreme fright or panic. This can immobilize a person who feels horror from an accident or an emergency. A heart attack, or the onset of a serious illness could also bring this state of mind. Panic attacks might also come under this heading.

The next three are not normally as intense . . . but they can be.

Aspen is for unspecific fears from an unknown origin. This is an uneasiness or foreboding about something . . . the person isn't sure what. Anxiety or apprehension best describe this state.

Mimulus can be for specific fears or phobias. People know exactly what it is they are afraid of. This Remedy is also for timid, shy people who are always nervous or frightened about something.

Red Chestnut is over-concern for others. This is the "mother syndrome" in which any delay or illness has got to mean the worst for loved ones. This is anticipating fear . . . nothing has happened yet. Still, it can drain energy and upset others.

So long as our Souls and personalities are in harmony, all is joy and peace, happiness and health. It is when our personalities are led astray from the path laid down by the Soul, either by our own worldly desires, or by the persuasion of others, that a conflict arises. This conflict is the root cause of disease and unhappiness.

-- Edward Bach M.D. in *Heal Thyself*

Children

Each stage of a child's life often seems to be radically different from the previous one. Fortunately, there are Bach Remedies for every mental state and children respond marvelously. Study the child and study the remedies and you will know what is right for today . . . tomorrow may be another need. For each major change in life, use **Walnut**. Here are a few others that might help.

SLEEPING PROBLEMS are a frequent concern. **Rock Rose** is used for the terror of nightmares; **Mimulus** and/or **Aspen** for fear of the dark; **Chicory** if the child's sleeping problem is only to get attention. **White Chestnut** is for insomnia and **Vervain** is for the wound up child, (avoiding sugar for three hours before bedtime also helps). Give **Walnut** if the child will be sleeping in other than his/her own bed.

A VERY SHY child would be helped by **Mimulus** while a lonesome child could use **Water Violet**. It would also help the child who wishes to play alone and needs to learn social skills. **Clematis** is for the spacy child who always lives in an imaginary world of daydreams.

LEARNING DIFFICULTIES stem from many causes including poor diet and insufficient sleep. But for those children who have to keep repeating the same lessons, **Chestnut Bud** is excellent. **Clematis** could also be needed here (see above). If there is no motivation to learn, use **Wild Rose**. If they won't try because they have no self-confidence, **Larch** is the answer. For those who are easily discouraged and give up easily, try **Gentian.**

HYPERACTIVE CHILDREN can also be the result of several causes but **Vervain** would always be recommended for the intense, always on-the-go young one. If they are easily irritated, try **Impatiens**. **Rescue** has a calming influence on many, possibly because of **Cherry Plum** which helps those out of control. If the cause is food or environmental, use **Walnut** and **Crab Apple**. The latter also helps with detoxification.

DIVORCE is very traumatic and **Star of Bethlehem** would always be called for. **Walnut** is important for the major changes taking place. Children often blame themselves and need **Pine** for guilt. **Holly** helps to keep the child loving and **Willow** can prevent resentment. **Elm** is for those feeling overburdened, and **Honeysuckle** for those who continue to live in the past.

This will give a small idea. But treat each child individually.

Animals and Remedies

Many animals are very important "family" members for they give us unconditional love. If we love them in return, we need to be aware of the wide variety of emotions they have. When they get into negative states, we need to "communicate" with our pets to understand what they're feeling. Put ourselves in the animal's place, so to speak.

A formula of three or four remedies can be made up for the animal and be put in drinking water or diluted and put in food. Two drops of concentrate can be put on nose or ears. As with people, the remedies should be given four times a day.

If there is a crisis, however, **Rescue Remedy** can be given internally or externally every two minutes at first and then over longer times as the animal becomes stable.

Since each animal has its own personality, the Remedies have to be selected individually. For instance, **Aspen** would be given for a nervous animal or skittish horse. **Chestnut Bud** is for the animal that is hard to train and keeps making the same mistakes.

For the animal that constantly demands attention, there is **Chicory**. **Wild Rose** could be used for the apathetic animal that just mopes around. (A veterinarian should also examine animals regularly.) The very timid, shy animal would profit from **Mimulus**.

Star of Bethlehem (or **Rescue**) would help an abused animal or one who has suffered injury or trauma of any kind. For the hyperactive, **Vervain** should be used. **Walnut** works very well whenever the animal has to be moved, or there is any change in environment or routine.

If a person reads over the information about the individual remedies with a pet in mind, it will soon be clear which ones would be useful. For a large animal, 10 drops at a time would be needed; work the amount down proportionately to size.

PLANTS

Walnut could help a transplanted plant; **Star of Bethlehem** would be for one that was drooping or traumatized with extreme cutting. **Rescue** is always safe. Just add drops to their regular water and see the improvement.

When Nothing Seems to Happen

There are times when a person can't see that the Remedies have helped. First, we check to see if the person is taking four drops four times a day. If they admit that they took it only twice, for three or four days, they hardly gave the Remedies a fair trial. If someone has seen instant relief from **Rescue,** they may have trouble understanding that deeper problems take some time.

Because the Remedies work so subtly, it is not always possible to see what is happening. For instance, one client found herself in a housecleaning frenzy while taking the Remedies. Part of her problem was that she was angry with her husband and her response had been to let the house go. As she got mentally and physically active, relationships began to improve.

Sometimes, it is just a gentle thought that keeps coming to you until finally it's, "OK! I'll take care of it!" Situations then improve. Or, a person may become more aware of their faults. For instance, a person taking **Beech** would say something critical and then be aware of what they did. Gradually, this awareness brings a change.

When one client told me she didn't see the Remedies had helped, I had to laugh. "Your whole life has changed in three weeks, I reminded her. She had stopped drinking, joined AA, gone on a serious diet and exercise program and gone back to church for the first time in four years. Actually, the results were amazing.

If a person seems to need a great number of Remedies, Dr. Bach said the solution was to give **Wild Oats** and/or **Holly.** This would also be true if the Remedies seemed not to work. After taking these, he said it would then become obvious just what specific Remedies were needed. He also said, "In cases where the person is of the active, intense type, give **Holly.** In patients who are of the weak, despondent type, give **Wild Oats.**" If in doubt, give both.

(See other possibilities on pages 19 and 20.)

How to Prepare Bach Remedies

Dr. Bach wanted to keep everything simple . . . and it is. Just remember that you are working with vibrational essences and they uplift mentally and spiritually. Have great respect for what you are doing. Do not have others in the room to distract you.

1. Center yourself. Get rid of all distractions. You are doing important work.
2. Take a glass pipette out of a 1 oz. brown dropper bottle and put it on a clean/sterile surface or in a baggie.
3. Fill bottle with **spring** water or **well filtered** water (3 filter reverse osmosis system is best). Do **not** use distilled water.
4. Take out all the Bach stock bottles you are going to use. Make sure you have the right ones. CHECK!
5. Take 2 drops from each stock bottle and put into your 1 oz. bottle. (4 drops if you are using **Rescue**)
6. As you use a stock bottle, put it back into your kit. This prevents your omitting a remedy . . . or putting it in twice. Some sources suggest adding a teaspoon of plain brandy to your bottle. Because of the large number allergic to alcohol, I never have. Using a teaspoon of apple cider vinegar is another option. By using pure water, however, I find this is also unnecessary.
7. Bless the Remedies before or after you put the pipette back in the bottle. You might also bless anyone who will take the Remedies.
8. Gently shake the bottle **vertically** about 5 times.
9. Write out a label with the person's name and "Take 4 drops 4 times a day." If it is Rescue, put "Take 4 drops as needed for trauma." Attach to bottle and secure with scotch tape. I put bottle in a baggie.
10. On a 3 x 5 card, record the name of the person the Remedies are for. Put the date, any special circumstances this formula was needed for and the formula. Put a line and list others that could have been used but there wasn't room for. This will be of help the next time the person needs Remedies.

11. Put an ounce or two of water in a glass and bring to the person who will be taking the Remedies. Show them how to put four drops in the water and have them drink it. Show them on the bottle where it is written, "Four drops four times a day." This may seem childish, but people have so much on their minds that I find emphasis helps. I then explain that it is best to take the drops in water or juice as they could touch the pipette with their mouth otherwise. Since we have acids around our mouth, it might spoil the formula. Of course, if they are an **Impatiens,** make sure they know they can drop the Remedies right into their mouths and hold the drops under their tongue for a few seconds. You might not get an **Impatiens** to take them any other way.

Reiterate all the great positive things that will happen to them as a result of taking the Remedies. MOTIVATE! Giving them a hug is a nice farewell gesture.

AGRIMONY
Cheerful Exterior; Painful Interior

YOU NEED AGRIMONY IF:

Someone asks, "How are you?" You ALWAYS reply, "Fine!" or "Great!" . . . with a big smile. Actually, you are mentally devastated and torn up inside.

Normally you dislike being alone so you try your best to be fun and the life of the party. You may have a lot of friends because you are fun to be with.

Life is so painful, however, you might resort to alcohol or drugs to dull the torture. Your thoughts may keep you awake at night and so you are very tired. (also see **White Chestnut** for insomnia)

Peace loving, you are distressed by quarrels or arguments. Possibly into denial. Not easy for you to share your inner self.

WHAT IT DOES FOR YOU:

A genuine optimist, you can put problems in perspective. You have such a good sense of humor, you can make jokes about illnesses, worries or pain.

People really enjoy being with you and are willing to share any of your heartaches. As you learn to trust others, and can discuss your problems, it will help dissolve the torment you lived with.

You may still be restless, and like excitement, but it will not take such dangerous directions as it might have before.

With a mind at rest, you will sleep better, feel better and handle problems as challenges. As a peacemaker, your talents can now be put to good use.

Rarely will a person have **all** of the symptoms indicated. Even one negative aspect can have a significant affect on a person's life, however, and so that Remedy should be used.

It's hard to believe AGGIE just lost his job, needs a
gall bladder operation and has the tax people after him.

ASPEN
Anxieties; Apprehension

WHAT IT'S NEEDED FOR:

Terrified of something about to happen. Don't know what they are afraid of, so often ashamed to tell anyone.

Usually alone, but sometimes in a group, has sudden panic attacks. Can result in trembling, cold sweats, butterfly stomach, palpitations, nausea, nervousness. Exteremely sensitive people who don't know how to access spiritual forces, may sense some impending disaster. Even traffic, noise, conflicts can trigger emotional panic.

In the weeks after trauma such as rape, muggings, burglaries, etc., fear of the unknown can cause serious anxieties. Horror trips from drugs or alcohol may produce the same effects. May want to take **Aspen** with **Rescue.**

Overactive imaginations; terror may involve thoughts of religion or death. (May also need **Clematis** for clear thinking.)

Fears after a serious illness such as cancer, heart attack or an accident. Since vitality is sapped by such fear, may need **Olive** too.

Emotional or physical panic may occur in the day but more often in the dark or after a nightmare. With children, may also fear being alone at night.

THE RESULTS ARE:

Inner confidence, strength returns. Able to face any situation; enjoys adventure, new experiences.

Aware that there is only one Power in the universe: Divine Love and they are safe. Trusting.

Those who are sensitive can easily tune to non-material planes of consciousness--possibly clairvoyants (clear seeing). They have what may be called: Inner Knowing or obtaining Word of Knowledge or Psychic ability. Using this insight into higher spiritual consciousness for the benefit of mankind, they make good teachers, therapists, guides.

Dr. Bach wrote of the positive **Aspen:** "Fearlessness because of the knowledge that the universal power of love stands behind all. Once we come to that realization, we are beyond pain and suffering, beyond care or worry or fear; we are beyond everything except the joy of life, the joy of death, and the joy of our immortality."

Love lets go of fear. Children may feel safe in an awareness of the protection of a Guardian Angel or Spirit Guide. Helpful to pray; "The Light of God surrounds me; the love of God enfolds me."

Aspen may be used externally also if the fear engenders a physical symptom such as hives. For specific fears use **Mimulus.**

Just where has your ASS BEEN?

BEECH
Overly Critical

WHAT IT'S NEEDED FOR:

Constant complainer; intolerant; judgmental. Picky-picky. Little things about others or situations easily upsets. Wants others to think as they do.

Often low self-esteem has caused suppression of own feelings and doesn't understand others. May shut off voice of Higher Self.

May be perfectionists; meticulous about selves or their work. Narrow-minded, hard on others (white glove treatment). Needs to be right. Always finds the "pea in the mattress." Kids who complain about food, school, everything else.

Intolerance to foods, climate, allergens, noise, animals, etc. Severe task-masters (**Vine** also if dominating). Tense inside. May cause headaches, indigestion, arthritis, M.S.

Annoyances and fault finding may leave them isolated and lonely.

THE RESULTS ARE:

Balanced judgment. Sympathetic, tolerant, sensitive. Overlooks small mistakes.

Looks for the good in others and allows them to develop according to their inner potential.

Develops a sense of humor. Lets people go their own way. Easier to live with.

A good Remedy when traveling as usually some things aren't quite as planned. Keeps a positive attitude.

Sees own faults and admits them thus opening a greater potential for true knowledge.

Works to try and understand others by mentally putting self in their position.

Better understands:
LIGHTEN UP . . .
EVERYTHING'S PERFECT

Dr. Bach said the Beech in perfection was Jesus, being crucified, saying, "Father, forgive them, for they know not what they do." Dr. Bach wrote, "It is obvious that none of us is in a position to judge or criticize, for the wisest of us sees and knows only the minutest fragment of the Great Scheme of all things, and we cannot judge, knowing so little, how the Great Plan will work."

CENTAURY
Weak Willpower; Timid Doormat

WHAT IT'S NEEDED FOR:

A person who enjoys serving, taking care of others, the "Marthas" of the world. However, because of eagerness, is easily taken advantage of as a volunteer, or by fellow workers, family or stronger personalities.

The "yes" man or woman who is easily exploited. May also be codependent.

Avoids arguments; doesn't stand up for self. May start to feel like a doormat, especially if not given enough praise and recognition.

Can't say "no" to peer pressure. What will the neighbors (family, others) think?

In a desire to help, takes on too much. Becomes tired, overworked. Perhaps needs **Hornbeam** too. May lose own personality and ability to grow.

Gives in to spoiled children, spouse. Suppresses own needs. Bound to family . . . perhaps to an ailing or dominating parent. Becomes a servant, slave, martyr instead of a cheerful helper. (**Also Willow and/or Walnut**)

Blindly follows gifted teachers, leaders. "I'm nobody."

THE RESULTS ARE:

Kind, quiet, gentle but with self-determination. New vitality and strength to mind and body.

Enjoys helping and serving but keeps a balance. Stands up for own needs. Enhances the magnificent virtue of being a willing, cheerful helper and/or volunteer with dedication to a cause.

Possibly the most sensitive of the personality types. Can be easily hurt in the negative but looks to the Spirit instead of the ego in the positive. Follows Inner Guidance.

Never a problem to employers or family. Good natured, pleasant, integrates well but develops own individuality and personality.

Centaury can make a personality stronger when trying to give up cigarettes, alcohol, drugs, poor food choices, etc.

No longer "volunteered to death" but decides things for self and does not overestimate abilities.

Takes away the timidity when "tough love" is necessary in any family situation.

I didn't think this was what I was volunteering for.

CERATO
Always Needs Others' Advice

WHAT IT'S NEEDED FOR:

Not sufficient confidence in themselves to make their own decisions. Constantly seeking advice from others. May be misguided.

Easily influenced . . . may also need **Wild Oats** if decisions involve life's goals.

Asks so many questions may tire others or get on their nerves.

Has many interests and acquires much knowledge but is too insecure to use it.

Follows majority thinking regardless of own beliefs. Might even imitate others.

Gets little done because of constant distractions and indecisions. Makes the simple complicated.

Always trying a new fad or option: clothes, diets, philosophies, health treatments or practitioners, etc.

May purchase or do something against own rational judgment and appear foolish. "I knew I shouldn't have."

May be endlessly on the phone. Needs to make several calls for one appointment.

Mind digresses because of so many interests and may have short attention span.

THE RESULTS ARE:

More centered, not ruled by emotions. Asks advice but then uses common sense.

Self-confident with minds of their own. Very knowledgeable; quiet certainty.

Trusts own Inner Guidance; perhaps very intuitive. Eager to learn but utilizes information and able to accomplish much more.

Has many interests but zeros in on less things so can succeed at what interests most.

Admires talented but not constantly concerned with what's "in." Sticks with decisions and convictions.

Parents can aid their children by encouraging them to make their own decisions. **Cerato** can help parents over-inclined to constantly tell young ones what to do.

Rarely will a person have **all** the symptoms indicated. Even one negative aspect can have a significant affect on a person's life and that Remedy can, therefore, be called for.

Yes, SIR OTTO, I've checked your stocks again today.
Everything's fine.

CHERRY PLUM
Desperate; Not in Control

WHAT IT'S NEEDED FOR:

Overstrained mind. Great danger of doing something irrational such as suicide. Could also be murderous impulses.

This is an extreme Remedy. It is in Rescue and other Remedies found there such as the patience (Impatiens) and clear, calm thinking (Clematis) are usually beneficial.

A holding in of energy through fear, such as at work or in service, makes a person want to "blow up."

Fear of being a child or spouse abuser. Children frustrated and screaming, banging heads, throwing things, vomiting and even bed wetting. Can't keep it in.

Verge of nervous breakdown; despair from long physical or mental suffering. (also **Elm** for overwhelmed).

Good support for any addiction rehabilitation where something was controlling a person.

Fear of "going mad" or doing something terrible that will bring lasting regret and perhaps cause being locked up.

Hysterical or deeply depressed . . . ˙if alternating, add **Scleranthus.** Deep fears such as agoraphobia (open places) or even of over-eating. Feeling possessed and controlled by outside energies or dark forces (spirit release therapy can help also).

Prisoners of state, on a job and/or at home. High strung, battle weary or shell-shocked souls out of control.

THE RESULTS ARE:

Composure. Energies tapped off before they explode or go into a rage.

Courage, strength, able to bear extreme adversities.

Remembers AAA . . . Action Absorbs Anxiety. Does physical things which let off steam.

Realized that they have reacted with fear because they have turned away from their Higher Guidance. Tries to understand what lessons they have learned and grow spiritually and mentally. They are led through darkness and chaos to a feeling of Divine Love and peace.

Uncontrollable tics, body spasms or coughing may dissipate and disappear.

Thank you, C.P. That certainly was a good example
of being out of control.

CHESTNUT BUD
Repeats Mistakes and Same Difficulties

WHAT IT'S NEEDED FOR:

Takes a longer time than others to learn the lessons of daily life. Doesn't take full advantage of observation and experiences. Needs more repetition than others.

This applies whether it is a school-child who is slow at math or a business person who has the same financial problems over and over because the mode of operation doesn't change.

Also applies to job jumping, marriage or relationship changing where the person ends up in the same type of situation.

This person may not be particularly unhappy. In fact, might be happy-go-lucky but seems frozen in a time warp. Doesn't face self or the past and so doesn't know how to build a future.

Some reasons: hurry (**Impatiens**); inattentiveness or lack of observation (**Clematis**). May also need **Walnut** for link breaking.

May be stubborn; refuses to listen to own inner guide and/or wants to do "own thing" rather than flow with the life process. This self-willed person is not cooperating in the school of life.

Blocks out unpleasant experiences. May be into denial and/or addiction.

THE RESULTS ARE:

Helps memory retention; assists in learning life's lessons. Understands the future is the mirror of the past and we cannot ignore it.

More aware of what's happening around us and can become a problem solver. Willing to get other points of view and to see self as others do.

Fast learner, absorbs information easily, is flexible. Observes own errors; watches and learns from others.

Grounded in the present; aware of the past; plans for the future.

Flows with life's plan and no longer repeats same difficulties, errors and actual mistakes.

No longer rushes into the new without absorbing effects from the past. Makes clear assessments.

Is alert enough not to be taken advantage of as happened in the past

Frequent examination of self with a view to improve and change. Learns from every experience of life.

* * *

One definition of insanity: Always doing the same things over but expecting different results. Denial of obvious realities.

48

CHICORY
Demands Attention; Martyrs

WHAT IT'S NEEDED FOR:

"Poor little me, " is the Chicory refrain. The egotist who can only take love in . . . like a human sponge. Easily feels hurt and rejected.

As children or adults, can be very manipulative: can manifest ailments, tears, tantrums.

No peace for the recipient of this smother love for there are always more demands for attention.

Naggers, may be critical (may need **Beech** too). Likes loved ones always around. Mothers may be upset at children going off to school; husbands don't want wives to go to own activities without them; child may cling, never want to share toys or parents. Irritable, strong-willed.

Even selfless people may need **Chicory** when giving up an addiction such as cigarettes, or going on a diet. Keeps them from feeling sorry for themselves.

Congested mentally and physically: sinus, colds, runny noses.

The over-bearing, critical parent or boss may also need **Vine.** As over-possessing, controlling directors of lives, **Chicory** people may be constantly directing, organizing ways to put the world right.

THE RESULTS ARE:

Has desire to serve others but does so with a selfless love. Allows others to develop and grow at their own rate.

Works without thought of personal gain. Truly dedicated to the interests of others, becomes what Dr. Bach called, "the universal mother." (can be male too)

In their helpfulness, they may be excellent organizers and good detail people.

Taken by those who are the object of a **Chicory** personality, it will help free them from being victims of manipulation.

Develops warmth, kindness, sensitivity and the ability to always see good growing in others. May even be able to bring out others' talents because of their attention and loving concern.

Great inner strength and feel secure in themselves. Find it easy to forgive and forget real or imagined offenses against them.

Can help free the addictive to feeling free and good about selves instead of "poor little me."

51

CLEMATIS
For Clear Thinking; Procrastinators

WHAT IT'S NEEDED FOR:

The daydreamers of life who live in their own fantasy world. If they live in the past, add **Honeysuckle.** If they live in the future, they may withdraw from problems or have impractical solutions.

Absent minded "professor" of any age, they may lose things, seem scatterbrained, confused.

TV addicts or forever lost in fiction. Heavy sleepers who may fall asleep at inappropriate times.

Never violent; rarely anxious. The **Clematis** type will agree, "You're probably right," because doesn't want to think about or discuss it.

Often has poor coordination . . . runs into doors, etc. Pale, cold hands and feet from poor circulation.

Memory? Details? "Now what did I come in here for?" Not too involved with physical reality. In fact, may not be too interested in life. Dr. Bach said this was, "a polite form of suicide."

Anyone preoccupied with inner problems, or indifferent workers. They withdraw into their own imagination.

THE RESULTS ARE:

Masters of their own thoughts, they are mentally alert and focused on their present projects.

Also called, the "Traveler's Joy," **Clematis** is great when driving long distances or on vacation.

Puts a "tiger in their tank" mentally, so that they can create from their thoughts which can be beautiful and sensitive. Inspired writers, artists, musicians, designers, actors, craftsmen, healers and, well sometimes, eccentrics.

The future is shaped in the present and their ideas will be our future. They open up to their mission here and feel part of the spiritual whole. **Clematis** may also aid in prayer and meditation.

Since they are more attuned "inside," they may have had trouble with sight and hearing until aided by **Clematis.**

They need sleep, light and sun. Since **Clematis** strengthens the bonds between the physical and our other levels, it may help to fight off infections.

In case of fainting or loss of consciousness, rub it on gums, behind ears, on wrists and palms.

I'm at the wrong house? Oh, yes, you're right.
Where's my mind today?

CRAB APPLE
Mental, Physical Cleanser; Dislikes Self

WHAT IT'S NEEDED FOR:

Feeling mentally or physically unclean. May be ashamed of thoughts or something done against basic beliefs.

May be unable to break a bad habit. Self-disgust. Or may be ashamed of alcoholic or filthy parents.

Good when fasting or detoxifying from cigarettes, alcohol or drugs (street or medicinal). For colds or any illness, especially contagious ones.

Sensitive to appearance. Disgusted because of body odors, smelly feet, vaginal or urine discharge, diarrhea, bad breath, passing gas frequently, constipation, excessive sweating, heavy menstrual periods, etc.

Cleaning phobias of house or self. Over-frequent washing, showering, mouth washes. May concentrate on trivial matters and ignore some really serious situations.

Crab Apple can also be used externally as a lotion for psoriasis, eczema, zits, rashes, scars or other skin conditions. People often feel depressed or despairing with Crab Apple conditions.

Helpful for rape victims; those who have had abortions; sometimes even pregnancy; any overweight condition.

THE RESULTS ARE:

Has a better, more balanced view of life. Feels at peace with self. With the inner harmony, physical disorders can leave.

School children won't despair because they haven't the right kind of "in" shoes or jacket or haircut.

There is a unique double action with Crab Apple in that it purifies mentally and physically. Accepts that man is a perfectly created spiritual being and physical problems will dissipate as lessons are learned.

> GREAT WITH RESCUE AS AN EYE WASH. SOOTHES TIRED, INFLAMED OR ALLERGY IRRITATED EYES.

Rescue and Crab Apple can be used for animals with fleas or insect-infested plants.

There may be a "healing crisis" in which everything first gets worse while the toxins are coming out. The end result, however, is vast improvement.

Add 10 drops of Crab Apple to a bath. Can also take 4 drops every ½ hour for flu, coughs, pollen or environmental allergies, hangovers, etc.

Of course I want you to be proud of your profession, Howard. It's just that I thought you were changing for our date.

ELM
Temporarily Overwhelmed

WHAT IT'S NEEDED FOR:

Too much responsibility just overwhelms a person. Very capable but there is TOO MUCH to do and feels unequal to the tasks ahead. May cause depression and exhaustion (**Hornbeam** also).

The situation is somewhat temporary but, at present, there is a faltering of self-confidence.

Painfully aware that their failure will adversely affect others . . . whether he/she is a head of state, a company, a household or a volunteer organization.

For weak moments in the lives of the strong. For a time, judgment is clouded, past successes forgotten and their brain feels foggy.

May cause a churning mind and sleeplessness (add **White Chestnut**).

The **Elm** type has usually consciously chosen the type of work or activity they are doing . . . and enjoys it. However, physical limitations, sudden personal problems, looming deadlines or everything coming at once, makes the pressure too heavy.

For some, just an overwhelming task like cleaning the basement or garage, not to mention passing a big exam, can distort perspective and bring deep gloom.

THE RESULTS ARE:

Self-confidence returns and determines the impossible is going to take only slightly longer.

The pressures of life are de-stressed and the person thinks clearly again.

Develops a clearer understanding that moderation in life is important to them. (may also need **Vervain**) May schedule a vacation time or days off, realizing the world just might go on for a short time without them. Doesn't take a beeper with them.

May be natural leaders and their positive, assured attitude helps others to be more relaxed and confident.

Knows that all the tasks may not be humanly possibly but can call on Divine Guide to assist and give strength.

Elm people frequently are involved in work for the betterment of others and they have high ideals. In the positive they are able to put problems and life into a larger perspective.

Super moms, teachers, clergymen, health care givers, etc., may all need **Elm** at times.

I just can't take one more straw.

GENTIAN
Easily Discouraged

WHAT IT'S NEEDED FOR:

May be the eternal pessimist, a "doubting Thomas," or just easily disheartened. Always, the cause of depression or discouragement is known.

Some people expect things to go wrong (Murphy's Law people). They blame external circumstances as opposed to the **Larch** person who simply lacks confidence in self.

While the **Gentian** condition may be relatively short-lived, it can be a disturbing depression. Since it can block mental and spiritual energies, a person may also need **Hornbeam** or **Olive** for tiredness or exhaustion.

A setback in an illness, a job difficulty, a financial downturn, etc., may cause dejection.

Excellent for discouraged school children, upset with lessons or exams. May also need **Wild Rose** if a person becomes apathetic and won't even try anymore.

For those fighting for faith; can't accept a belief system although wants to. May even need faith in Bach. Possibly too mental . . . analyzing, questioning. "Oh Lord, help thou my unbelief."

Good for convalescing, for the worried elderly, the discouraged dieter, nervous athletes, pooped-out parents.

THE RESULTS ARE:

Cheerful, contented, emotionally stable with an unshakable confidence that all challenges in life have a solution.

Has faith in Divine help and/or in the process of life. Understands that everything has a deeper meaning and sees difficulties as part of the human learning process.

Knows a negative state of mind can attract unpleasant situations. Also aware that a person's discouragement affects not only self but those around him/her.

There is no failure for those who have tried their best. The success is for those who have tried; the failures for those unwilling to attempt.

Wonderful for those who can't get or afford psychotherapy.

A sense of peace removes anxiety and helps one see Light at the end of a dark tunnel.

Becomes an optimist, believing in ultimate success or perfect solutions. Attracts others who are needed for the right answers.

GORSE
Hopelessness; Depression

WHAT IT'S NEEDED FOR:

Pessimistic outlook; feels there is no hope . . . nothing can be done. Convinced there is no sense in trying but will make the effort if prodded by family, friends. It is a passive resistance.

This situation can occur if the doctor has said, "You have to live with it," or, worse, given the patient a death sentence.

Many have overcome these pronouncements, but not in the Gorse state. Many know, "There are no incurable diseases; only incurable patients."

Chronic or genetic illnesses can bring on this depression. Also, if a person has tried many different treatments and none have been successful, becomes resigned. "Oh, I've tried everything but . . ."

Will have no confidence in Bach Remedies but will take just to please the care-giver.

Negative expectations will bring down the immune system and allow the illness to become more entrenched. No energy to try.

Some with only minor ailments can make them worse with depression. Gorse people may have dark circles under their eyes (possibly stress in adrenals or kidneys).

THE RESULTS ARE:

Gorse can set the process of healing in motion, especially if given early for chronic illnesses. A sense of hope and joy begins to return which is the first step to recovery.

This can be the turning point when a person develops a new attitude. Taking one day at a time and agreeing to "never say never," faith can be revitalized.

They don't expect the impossible and achieve a state of peace even with a fatal illness.

They are not influenced by the negative opinions of doctors or others.

Recovery is from the inside out and the body will quickly respond and be re-energized by a positive, hopeful outlook.

Since we learn most through trials and painful experiences, this can be a new growth step. It can also arm us to oppose dark energy forces. We can overcome all with Divine assistance.

The Gorse person is more depressed than a Gentian but not in the total despair of the Sweet Chestnut.

And you know the worst part, GORSE . . . <u>now</u> I've got an itch.

HEATHER
Obsessed With Own Problems

WHAT IT'S NEEDED FOR:

Always talking about themselves, they are poor listeners. Brings conversation back to selves consistently. Self-centered.

Full of self-concerns and bore you with every trivia of their lives. Nothing is ever explained in one sentence . . . it takes a looooong monologue.

May be the class clown; have a Madonna complex. Wants your undivided attention. Emotional child state.

In a group or class will constantly ask questions or monopolize the conversation. If allowed to talk, will make story a long, drawn-out affair.

They have no inner peace and may be on your energy field, sapping your energy. Can be hypochondriacs.

May be on the phone incessantly. Gets little done because of preoccupation with what they perceive as their mountainous problems (which may be molehills).

Does not easily let go: holds your arm or stands in your way so you can't escape. Talks ad nauseum; usually boring. No interest in problems of others. Dislikes being alone.

THE RESULTS ARE:

Good listeners and develops many more friends. Gradually becomes selfless and understanding of others. A readiness to help.

Sees their problems in perspective and realizes they shouldn't dump them on everyone else.

Enjoys quiet time. Can build interior strength and/or spiritually develops.

Helps children to learn to play alone and not always insist on being the focal point of attention. Can carry on a two-way conversation with give and take. Isn't such a whirlwind talker.

Gets much more accomplished as interest grows for many things outside of self.

Great empathy and works in a quiet atmosphere of strength and self-confidence.

Easily confused with **Chicory** who give in order to get and feel sorry for selves.

Heather people don't have time (or think about) giving to others. Not usually self-pity. However, a person can be both.

Did I tell you about my operation?

HOLLY
Hatred, Jealous, Envious

WHAT IT'S NEEDED FOR:

The opposite of love in any form. Hatred, jealousy and envy but also anger, suspicion and a desire to attack. For revenge. This can be mentally or verbally and, perhaps, even in the subconsious.

Also intolerance, distrust, greed, misunderstandings, judgments, etc. Do not have a peaceful energy. May be quick tempered and argumentative. Can hate self.

These powerful feelings may cause serious illness. They may result from not feeling loved, grave disappointment, or being hard-hearted.

These feelings are the most significant cause for all personal and worldwide difficulties and problems. They separate God from man. Probably no one is entirely free from these negative feelings.

Use for siblings and animals when there is a new baby. When going through the stage of anger after a loved one dies. When trying to grow on a spiritual path.

THE RESULTS ARE:

The highest vibrational essence, Holly brings us closer to the ideal state of unconditional love. In this we approach the all encompassing love of the Divine. It is thus the greatest healing power as well as the strongest motivational force.

While Holly is an antidote for hatred, it can, on a larger scale, gradually bring a person so into the positive that the heart is completely open.

With this there is inner harmony and peace and a nurturing, caring personality emerges. In the uniting with Divine Love, everyone is seen as a brother or sister and, as part of us, there is a rejoicing at the progress and success of others.

Holly is most helpful for anyone trying to advance on the spiritual path. And, since "Perfect love casts out fear," it helps to dissolve the personal fears that result from any absence of love.

Good for children to help them to share and play together in greater harmony.

Holly also protects us from hatred and everything that is not love.

Dr. Bach wrote: "If ever a case suggests that it needs many Remedies, or if ever a case does not respond to treatment, give either Holly or Wild Oats, and it will then be obvious which other Remedies may be required."

She's getting pizza _again,_ HOLLY! I think she's in those fancy
clothes just to get the delivery guy's attention.

HONEYSUCKLE
Living in the Past

WHAT IT'S NEEDED FOR:

A nostalgia for the past which consumes vital forces and makes one lose interest in the present.

Can be a house move . . . "When I was still at . . ." keeps a person from adjusting to change and making new friends.

Not just for the aged. A homesick nursery school child who can't adjust. Or even on the first day of school for child and/or parent.

For weeks, months after the death of a loved one, when there are still no signs of adjustment.

Always memories of youth (and perhaps glamour). May even dress as though were still younger. Dwelling in the past can actually accelerate aging as energy wanes. With stagnation, toxins accumulate. (May also need **Crab Apple**)

Regrets and sorrows from the past. If can't let go of a situation, may also need **White Chestnut.**

With unfulfilled hopes, can be tired and depressed (also **Hornbeam**) and, sometimes, full of self-pity (add **Chicory**). If certain memories are fearful, such as war experiences, may also need **Mimulus.**

Lives in past so won't have to confront present problems. Wants to control own future with no changes.

THE RESULTS ARE:

Lives in the NOW. Symptoms disappear from past traumas. Can sleep peacefully.

Capable of change. Knows lessons are taught to us by the past. Sees what was beautiful but does not cling to the memories. Profits from them in living an exciting and a vital present.

The dying are able to let go of life more easily, peacefully.

Counteracts wishes, influences and desires of the past which have been causing sorrow. No regrets.

Gets busy with work, hobbies, friends, and becomes more cheerful, happy. Accepts that there is always change in life and goes with the flow.

Doesn't glorify the past . . . especially when putting down everything in the present.

Accepts whatever age they are at chronologically and works to be mentally youthful.

Clematis people have fantasies and look for a better future. **Honeysuckle** folks think the past was best . . . may fantasize about that.

Come back to the present!

Oh, HONEY, remember the good ol' days
before the government outlawed Eye of Newt
and Suckling Dragon's Scales?

HORNBEAM
Tired; Procrastination

WHAT IT'S NEEDED FOR:

Mental and physical fatigue but weariness comes from the mind. Burn-out; dull routine; dislikes job; too many demands and no time for fun.

Can also come from driving self too hard and too long whether it is studying, trying to get ahead or running a household.

May need stimulants to get going in the A.M. Just getting out of bed is an effort. Once the day progresses, usually manages to get work done. And, if there is a party or interesting event later, can really wake up.

After an illness, may be afraid to walk, exercise, return to work.

If eye problems, may not like what they are seeing in their life. **Hornbeam** can be put on a compress for the eyes, varicose veins, etc.

Procrastination can cause tiredness as avoiding a job becomes a stress. This can also happen if a person is in too much of a routine.

Eating too much, being too sedentary and gray days can also cause great fatigue.

Bored animals, limp plants and TGIF devotees can all benefit. If every day feels like Monday morning, use **Hornbeam**.

THE RESULTS ARE:

Like a tonic or cool shower, **Hornbeam** can invigorate and bring freshness of mind. Encouraged to arrange variety in life . . . a change of scenery or vacation.

With inner vitality, a person feels less fatigued and is able to "get out of the box" of stress and/or boredom.

Exercise can also help this person as they are now challenged out of their mental rut. Certain of their ability to do what life demands of them, they are no longer distressed.

They might work toward new goals, be more spontaneous in life and/or work with their Higher Self toward exciting growth.

Gets things done without waiting until the last minute. Doesn't live on nerves.

* * *

For total mental and physical exhaustion, use **Olive**.

Rarely will a person have **all** the symptoms indicated. Even one negative aspect can have a significant affect on a person's life and that Remedy can, therefore, be called for.

Should I blow the HORN again, Mr. BEAM?

IMPATIENS
Impatient, Irritable

WHAT IT'S NEEDED FOR:

Everything needs to be done quickly. Slow drivers, workers, talkers send them into orbits of frustration. They will even finish a sentence for you.

Although usually extroverted, they prefer to work alone, undisturbed. If they have employees (or children) under them, they can be slave drivers because they push others as well as themselves.

They can be curt and may even take a tool or something out of someone's hand if the person is too slow or awkward.

Because of mental and inner tension, it is Dr. Bach's suggestion for PAIN. (I also consider **Pine**.)

Although accident prone, they have such quick reactions that they may often avoid serious injury.

As part of the **Rescue** Remedy, it is beneficial in nervous, impatient situations such as awaiting news of tests, results from doctor or hospital. When recovering from illness or injury, **Impatiens** can aid in recovery by helping to relax, settle down.

Inner tension may cause indigestion or spasms. Also nervous drumming, foot movements, eating too often.

For any situation requiring patience: beating a deadline, moving, getting ready for vacation, learning a new skill, etc.

THE RESULTS ARE:

Still prefers speed, and is quick and efficient, but is more patient and settled. Adapts to the pace of others with calmness.

Less tense, their good humor is restored. They are more gentle and diplomatic with others. They are better teachers and parents.

They have great gifts and now are willing to use them helping others.

Good as entrepreneurs or where a worker is needed who can be self-reliant and independent. They are laid back enough, however, so that the less gifted can still feel good about themselves.

Since it is often difficult to keep **Impatiens** on the Remedies, let them know they can put them directly into their mouth, but without touching the pipette. They might not take time to put the drops in water/juice. Also **Impatiens** can be put in a spray bottle (possibly with other Remedies) and misted where there is pain or even tension in the air. Some would like to drop it on whole cities and "chill out" anger (or drivers in places like Rome).

Is not given to angry flare-ups (although short-lived, causes problems). The brilliant and ambitious need **Impatiens** at times, so it is probably not coincidental that it was the first Remedy Bach discovered.

Now you'll stop ringing, won't YOU?

LARCH
Doubts Own Abilities

WHAT IT'S NEEDED FOR:

"For those who do not consider themselves as good or as capable as those around them, who expect failure, who feel that they will never be a success, and so do not venture or make a strong enough attempt to succeed."

-Dr. Bach

Because of their lack of confidence in themselves, **Larch** people are often melancholy. They can applaud the success of others without the envy or jealousy that mark a **Holly** but they may be wistful.

Somehow they are negatively programmed . . . possibly from infancy, school or parents . . . to feel inferior. Such a certainty of failure is in their makeup, that they will automatically respond, "Oh, I couldn't do that!" whenever a suggestion for something new is presented to them.

By not attempting, they can't learn and their abilities (which are often considerable) can't develop. Long term and temporary problems can develop such as illness, nervous breakdown, sexual frigidity, etc.

They are more passive than frightened (**Mimulus**) and, although they feel like failures, won't take a risk or gamble. They acquire a self-limiting false modesty.

THE RESULTS ARE:

Larch instills confidence and helps them plunge into life. They acquire new joy and enthusiasm as they appreciate their own unique selves.

With a new attitude, they are willing to take initiatives and responsibilities. They know there will be some setbacks and failures but they persevere and begin to develop their true potential.

Although self-conscious at first, they will try new experiences: return to school, move, find a new job and/or relationship, join in competitive events, try for a promotion, etc.

Children are especially helped by **Larch** as they struggle to know their self-worth and accept themselves.

Adults get over the Rodney Dangerfield outlook as they learn that there can never be successes without failures. So, go for it! Love for others starts with a love of self and putting ego in proper perspective.

Useful before exams or starting something creative. Helps them "get out of the box" of life they were in.

* * *

Larch lacks confidence and becomes discouraged; **Gentian** is depressed only after things go wrong. Is aware of ability.

OF COURSE YOU CAN, LARCH. YOU HAVE TO START BELIEVING IN YOURSELF. I'LL SHOW YOU HOW EASY IT IS.
David B. Roth

MIMULUS

Fears from Known Causes, Shyness

WHAT IT'S NEEDED FOR:

All known anxieties or phobias... may also need to add **Rescue** at first if symptoms are severe.

Fears of everyday life . . . driving on the freeway; stern parents, teachers, employers; other "kinds" of people, cultures, places, foods.

Physically sensitive, may be shy, introverted; keeps to self. Or, to conceal nervousness, may be gabby, giggly, blushing, or stammering easily.

There are common fears: heights, water, flying, elevators or enclosed areas, doctors, dentists, injections, "catching" illnesses such as AIDS, cancer or even flu; accidents and death.

Babies who cling or cry on awakening. Those very dependent on parents, spouses, children.

Public speaking is such terror, may also need **Rock Rose**. Often afraid to tell others of fears.

May be fearful of certain other live things such as cats, dogs, mice, snakes, bugs, etc.

Fear of future, loss of income, poverty, growing old. Loudness or conflicts upset. Thunder, storms, high winds frighten.

May get stomach pains, headaches, "itis" or stress illnesses . . . colitis, arthritis, etc.

THE RESULTS ARE:

Learns to grow and overcome fears by facing them. Finally cured of long-standing anxieties. Fewer worries . . . greater happiness. As they let go, school or work improves dramatically.

Although they become bolder, they are basically peaceful types whose "rages" wouldn't scare a fly.

They understand their sensitive constitution and make allowances. Quiet time, their own space and occasional retreats will recharge them. Walking alone can help them in their need to be guided by the laws of their own soul.

They may discover an artistic nature for music, painting, writing, etc. Happily creating alone, they grow in confidence.

As one fear disappears, others follow. Their calm, peaceful demeanor makes them delightful companions. They understand and can help other fearful souls and guide them to take charge of their own minds.

If ill or hurt, they speed their recovery by being positive and unafraid to move, exercise, take charge of their minds and bodies.

They know they may not physically be able to do all that others do and that's OK. Being alone or in the dark is a time to relax, build up their inner strength.

But MIM, you only have _one_ word to say.

MUSTARD
Black Depression for Short Time

WHAT IT'S NEEDED FOR:

"For those who (have) times of gloom, or even despair as though a cold, dark cloud overshadowed them and hid the light and joy of life."   --Bach

There is no explanation for the **Mustard** state which may last a day or two or several. The cloud leaves just as inexplicably as it came.

It has been blamed on P.M.S., hormonal imbalance and dark energy forces. (demonic?) Sometimes, gloomy weather might be responsible. Certainly it is strong and devastating while it lasts.

Depression arrives suddenly, without reason, and also lifts of its own accord. A person can then become fearful of its return.

While in this dark state, a person may cry without reason, be unable to hardly move or leave the house, be ineffective at work. Energies are drained and the depths of the soul are in mourning.

With no normal thoughts, they can't cover up their state of despair. In this hopeless, emotional state, it seems too encompassing to fight.

THE RESULTS ARE:

Peace and inner serenity return with **Mustard** which, for this state, is a real miracle of grace.

For some it is like slowly awakening from a dark, terrifying nightmare. Was it an illusion?

Freed from their painful prison, they can return to a normal life with relief and cheerfulness.

Dr. Bach said, "This Remedy dispels gloom and brings joy into life."

It has been said that the soul so craves its true source of Light that it can rise over the dark clouds. Spiritual development can then take another step forward as the attack is counteracted.

*   *   *

A spray mist that includes **Mustard** and **Rescue** could be sprayed in a funeral room or a place where someone is very ill. This way, all could benefit.

> Rarely will a person have **all** of the symptoms indicated. Even one negative aspect can have a significant effect on a person's life and that Remedy can, therefore, be called for.

He didn't have that cloud yesterday but I see it's back again.

OAK
Tired But Always Struggles On

WHAT IT'S NEEDED FOR:

Strength, endurance and a sense of obligation mark the stressful life of an **Oak**.

Although they have great courage and devotion to duty, too many tasks can prove to be overwhelming and they get to a state of chronic exhaustion.

They are too conscientious to complain ("It's my job") but the constant overwork takes away joy and can leave depression.

Very reliable, they can be a firm foundation at work or in the family. An executive type, a super mom, a single parent could all fall into this category. Even a student who works full time and still achieves high grades could be an **Oak**.

With life a constant struggle, even the superhuman **Oak** can crack. Heart attack, stroke, nervous collapse or mental breakdown can fell this brave soul. Because of their tremendous will power, they can be rigid and lose flexibility.

When their heart is no longer in their work, they stick to it but their inner life can suffer. There are high ideals but no joy and, possibly, no patience with others at this point. (add **Impatiens**)

THE RESULTS ARE:

With more common sense, they find inner pressures reducing and realize the need to pace themselves.

With more inner energy, they can become playful and willing to take time off. A new momentum develops.

Often strong in appearance, they are like the mighty **Oak** which only bends when other trees break.

Everyone may lean on them and they often make great contributions. They may even sustain a whole nation . . . such as the sturdy Churchill who inspired his country and growled, "Never give up!"

If an **Oak** becomes ill, they go down fighting as they always continue their efforts to find a cure or a new treatment.

They no longer wake up with hands and teeth clenched. Exercising neck and shoulders helps relieve stress.

They are upset if they can't meet their obligations, such as after a long illness. Recovery time is hard on them and their care-givers but **Oak** is a great help.

* * *

This is a Personality type Remedy. **Oak** people always have to watch that they are in the positive.

You've got to give OOAK credit.
He's determined and always hangs in there.

OLIVE
Total Exhaustion

WHAT IT'S NEEDED FOR:

Mental and physical exhaustion with no reserve strength. The adrenal glands are depleted.

Too tired for any pleasures. Nothing interests. Unable to cope anymore. The smallest job is a big chore. Should have a medical checkup.

This weak state can result from years of worry; chronic, long-term illness of self or being a caregiver for such a one.

Extended family, financial or job difficulties can sap the strength of the most hardy.

A new or sick baby or child, where there is never a good night's sleep, can drain parents.

Working on long, extended projects or ordeals can bring total weariness after a while. Depression is frequently a companion of an **Olive** person.

Some people can be made weak by poor diets, inadequate food or sleep. If lack of sleep is from constant worry and a churning mind, **White Chestnut** should also be given.

If there is mental confusion, which frequently accompanies deep tiredness, add **Clematis.** A hard-driving **Vervain** may also get into the **Olive** mode.

THE RESULTS ARE:

Since the time when the dove from Noah's ark returned with an Olive branch, the Olive tree has always been the symbol of peace and harmony.

In the Bach Remedy, it restores peace to the tired mind and vitality to an exhausted, suffering body. An interest in life returns.

A positive **Olive** can be seen in those recovering from a long illness, or forced to remain inactive, who still have an aura of peace about them and an active interest in many things.

Peaceful slumber may be another gift of the **Olive** remedy. This is a blessing for those with such a deep tiredness. A happy regeneration of energy allows people to restore balance to their world and see things clearly again. There may still be much stress but joy diminishes its effects.

Personal efforts often need extra help. **Olive** is a source of inner strength and nourishment. It brings the gentle assistance of Divine guidance. Energy returns.

I think OLIVE needs a rest.

PINE
Guilt - Pain

WHAT IT'S NEEDED FOR:

Blames self for not doing better - even when successful by most standards. Often hard working, over-consciencious.

Blames self for everything that goes wrong even when done by their children, employees, etc.

Continual stress and frustration which makes life joyless. They may always feel tired and depressed (add **White Chestnut** if can't sleep). Unable to accept themselves, they may have difficulty accepting a compliment. (Self disgust . . . add **Crab Apple**)

Uncomplaining scapegoats, may even feel need to apologize when ill. May feel they are being punished. May be accident prone or have other ways of punishing self. Abused children or spouses may feel they deserve poor treatment.

Always willing to try anything requested or needed and usually do well but not up to their own expectations.

Always apologizing. May feel ashamed. Continual stress, frustration may bring eating disorders or other illnesses.

Despite having many positive experiences, never content with efforts. May feel they can never please parents, spouse, employers, etc. Usually given for PAIN.

THE RESULTS ARE:

Takes things easier and learns to relax and enjoy life. Sound judgment; fair attitude. Recognizes self as a loved child of God.

Is willing to take responsibilities and bear the burdens of others only if they see they can really help them. Aware this is not always the best way to help another.

Knows errors and mistakes but doesn't dwell on them. Great perseverance but does not overburden self.

Becomes a more enjoyable, considerate partner, friend, employer. Understands their talents and accepts them with genuine humility. No regrets; total forgiveness . . . including self.

Dr. Bach wrote: "No great ascent was ever made without faults and falls, and they must be regarded as experiences which will help us to stumble less in the future. No thoughts of past errors must ever depress us; they are over and finished and the knowledge thus gained will help us avoid a repetition of them."

As God's beloved, know you deserve the best.

> Rarely will a person have **all** the symptoms indicated. Even one negative aspect can have a significant affect on a person's life and that Remedy can, therefore, be called for.

Oops? What do you mean "Oops"?

RED CHESTNUT
Over-Anxious for Others

WHAT IT'S NEEDED FOR:

Selfless in their concern for others, they are self-sacrificing and over-protective. Great attachment to those held dear.

"Mother hen" complex, worries and suffers needlessly for loved ones. If they're late, there is an accident; if ill it must be serious, etc.

If there is constant fear, **White Chestnut** may also be needed.

Worries about things that they cannot help with. Can be codependents.

Dr. Bach searched out **Red Chestnut** after he had an accident with an ax and those around him were so anxious that he experienced acute physical pain. They had not helped him, he said.

Can be helpful for those concerned with relatives in risky activities such as skiing, football, etc., or going on a long distance vacation.

Grandparents frequently need. For loved ones in pregnancy, childbirth or surgery.

Fear can retard development of those cared for as they feel and react to the negativity; especially if constant warnings are given. Helpful for weaning babies but for all ages.

THE RESULTS ARE:

Remains calm in all situations and is thus a blessing to those in accidents, illnesses or any distress.

Able to visualize a white light of God's protection surrounding loved ones and then relaxes and leaves them in His hands.

Has a solicitude and love for one's neighbors and is willing to help but not interfere.

Understands that fear harms ourselves as well as those we're concerned for and replaces the emotion with pure love. Helps to loosen anxiety bonds between couples, children, parents, etc., and replaces them with positive thoughts of well-being and security.

When anxious thoughts come, trains self to say and think positive thoughts such as: "We wish them well!"; "We know they'll be guided in the right way."; "I see God's angels protecting you."

With less anxiety, the person's health improves. They understand the power of thought.

Now stick together . . . there are hunters out there . . .
you might get lost . . . last week I saw a boy
with a fishing net . . . etc., etc.

ROCK ROSE
Terror, Panic

WHAT IT'S NEEDED FOR:

Extreme fright; panic attacks. Paralyzed with fear; all the senses rigid and numb.

Usually this is for a temporary condition but there is a great sense of urgency. Since it is part of the **Rescue Remedy, Rock Rose** is usually used in that form. It can be used externally also and is very effective in accidents or when someone is hysterical or has just had a terrorizing nightmare.

Dr. Bach said that it could even be used in situations where there appeared to be no hope.

Other times when it might be used: for hyperactive or tantrum inclined children; in severe weather conditions such as blizzards or hurricanes. Any other time when there is terror in the atmosphere. At such times, it should be taken every few minutes.

Flying, going to dentist or doctor, being in strange places will all cause terror to some.

Long term it helps those easily frightened; recovering from serious illness, attack, accident, burglary.

THE RESULTS ARE:

Courage, steadiness, dependability.

Self can be completely forgotten and a person may even be led to risk life and safety. This would be especially true in wartime or where there was a dangerous situation, mostly involving many people.

Deep breathing and protecting the solar plexus area with spiritual light are also recommended since it may feel like a kick in the stomach.

Rock Rose could help to bring someone out of a breathing crisis such as asthma.

A person mobilizes tremendous inner strength and energy.

Along with **Clematis** and **Impatiens,** also in **Rescue,** can help someone whose life is in turmoil and everything is happening too quickly.

Spiritually, those trying to advance can be helped through the "Dark Night of the soul."

Calms and mellows anyone under acute threat whether mental, physical or spiritual.

ROCKY, look at these beautiful ROSES. ROCKY?

ROCK WATER
Rigid Mind

WHAT IT'S NEEDED FOR:

Great inflexibility of belief system and life-style. Drives self to great lengths and gives up many common pleasures in pursuit of perfection.

This could be someone like Edison, who worked unceasingly, or like Gandhi who adopted an ascetic lifestyle to change political conditions. Dr. Bach was a hard taskmaster on himself. His goal was to ease the sufferings of mankind, but at times, he was very hard on himself.

Some **Rock Waters** live by the clock with a strict schedule that rarely changes. They may have programmed exercise into their day and this, too, would be done with iron discipline.

They have high ideals but, in practice, they can be stubborn and unyielding. This may be in regard to religious beliefs, politics, eating and lifestyle habits, work/study routines, etc. They are not good for discussions because their beliefs are the only right ones. At the extreme, they are fanatics. Forgiveness is difficult for them.

Concerned only with their own perfection, they don't interfere with others.

THE RESULTS ARE:

Pain turns to joy as they loosen up and acquire a sense of humor. They can now enjoy others. Can become adaptable idealists.

Not easily influenced but, at least, open-minded enough to listen to ideas and opinions of others. Will even adjust own beliefs if greater logic is presented. Becomes humbler and more easily approached. They forgive.

Can start dissolving illnesses caused by being tight and inflexible. Will exercise or play sports for fun instead of needing to have a training quota.

After some time, they can grow to be kind, gentle and patient and not concentrate on themselves. As they allow insights within to affect the outer person, they may find themselves working to be of service to others.

Becoming adaptable gives them an inner freedom and they can begin to bend mentally, physically and spiritually.

The joy and peace they now express will encourage others to follow far more than past stubbornness.

At times they will take life easy and enjoy some personal comforts.

* * *

Gold medals may be won by **Rock Waters** but life will have more joy when they can hang looser. **Rock Water** is a Personality Remedy.

But I _did_ buy her a washing machine.

SCLERANTHUS
Indecisive; Never Certain

WHAT IT'S NEEDED FOR:

Constantly changing mind between **two things.** Can be unreliable because will say "yes," then "no."

They keep the agonies of indecision pretty much to themselves, preferring to find own answers. (Unlike **Cerato** who asks everyone)

Their moods and feelings can also change rapidly: sad/happy, active/apathy, laugh/cry, high energy/exhausted, enthusiastic/disinterested, etc.

Time is wasted as they vacillate about jobs, schools, life style, proposals, moving and other important issues. But what to eat or wear, where to go and minor issues receive the same erratic attention.

They can't concentrate on a conversation because their grasshopper minds go back and forth between subjects.

Physically, their symptoms come and go but they may be subject to problems of balance: inner ear difficulties; car, air or seasickness. Carnival rides are definitely out for them.

Because of poor equilibrium, they may not do well in sports. May use jerky, nervous gestures. Children may be fidgeters. Poise and balance may not be good. Nervous tension, or even breakdown, possible.

As opinions change, they may feel an inner restlessness. If they start to feel inferior, would also need **Larch.**

THE RESULTS ARE:

Determination and good powers of concentration. Avoids extremes and keeps good balance and poise.

With a clearer direction, they can make decisions in their personal and business lives and stay with them.

They can decide to come for Bach or other treatments which will help them. Prioritizes activities and accomplishes much more.

Because they are more centered and have an inner calm, they have a peaceful effect on others.

They may become confident of their intuition and let their Inner Guide aid them in decision making. Soul development can then progress.

This Remedy stabilizes and gives flexibility but without ambiguity. With more inner strength, they make quick decisions and thus decide their futures.

Tell SCLER and THUS to stop changing their minds
about where to land.

STAR OF BETHLEHEM
Shock; Trauma

WHAT IT'S NEEDED FOR:

". . . great distress which for a time produces great unhappiness. The shock of serious news, the loss of someone dear, the fright following an accident, and such like . . . for a time refuse to be consoled."
-Dr. Bach

Can aid physical shocks to the body such as injury, sunburn, frostbite; even rape and muggings.

Mentally it can neutralize such emotional shocks as deaths, divorces, separation, loss of job, a serious quarrel.

It may be the most important Remedy in **Rescue**, for shock can often be repressed and appear as a physical problem years later. Trauma is held at the cellular level and can block many systems.

Good for newborns (plus **Walnut**) or for anyone going through rebirthing therapy. For children who are frightened, injured or abused.

For numbness, tenseness in stomach or throat; other nervous conditions.

As part of **Rescue,** aids those getting away from addictions.

THE RESULTS ARE:

Dr. Bach called it "The comforter and soother of pains and sorrows." It restores vitality, especially for nerves. Gives mental clarity and inner strength.

Important for conditions that resist treatment . . . there may be a deep trauma known only to the subconscious. Even helps psychosomatics.

Unbelievably miraculous for weddings, funerals and even proms.

ALWAYS USE STAR
THE FIRST TIME A PERSON
RECEIVES REMEDIES.

A trauma may have been yesterday or it may have been any time back to (and before) birth. **Star** cleanses out old traumas that are at the cellular level and blocking present progress. Childhood frights, war experiences and other traumas may be consciously blocked out. But they remain.

Star allows an opening of the personality to permit communication with its Higher Self.

As it facilitates quick recovery, always use in any accident or shock. Affirm that all energy blocks are dissolved.

Along with **Holly** and **Wild Oats,** is a general aid when specific problems are vague or not responding to other Remedies.

I know it was awesome,
but you must also admit it was traumatic.

SWEET CHESTNUT
Unbearable Anguish of Mind and Soul

WHAT IT'S NEEDED FOR:

"It is the Remedy for that terrible, that appalling mental despair when it seems the very soul itself is suffering destruction. It is the hopeless despair of those who feel they have reached the limit of their endurance."-Dr. Bach

The deepest depression of the Remedies, it is for the people at the end of their rope. They feel utterly lost, alone, helpless and empty.

They suffer intensely but with passivity, unlike the **Cherry Plum** people who are out of control and may commit suicide or murder.

Some causes for such grief: death of a spouse, child, close friend, pet. Facing a terminal illness, operation, loss of limb or sight, confinement to a wheelchair, addictions.

Family situations of abuse, adult children of alcoholics therapy, grandparents in total isolation or fearful for grandchildren. Abandonment, bankruptcy, job loss can also bring on this black depression in some.

May need **Olive** for the exhaustion in this acute state where not even death rescues them. Usually they find it impossible to even pray. In complete darkness, they feel only a void.

It is an emergency state for the soul for their absolute sorrow allows no joy, no peace. Wars and battles can bring on this mental torture. **White Chestnut** may also be needed for the mind constantly replaying thoughts and scenes.

THE RESULTS ARE:

At first there is only a thin ray of hope but the inner journey has started.

As release from their heartbreaking pain begins, it starts them on a new road of growth and personal development.

Help is actually nearest when the need is greatest, so as they look to the Father for help and begin to trust again, miracles happen.

They are aided through this difficult transition and become much stronger. Not inclined to tell their problems to others, they may also need **Agrimony**. The words, "Once I was lost and now I'm found," take on great meaning as they rise from the ashes of self-destruction.

Once stabilized, they can be of great help to others going through grief periods.

Walking in nature and in the light can be very beneficial in the healing. As hope and peace of mind return, they truly feel reborn.

Sweet Chestnut is even deeper than **Gorse** which can probably be considered medium depression. **Mustard** is also black depression but it comes and goes. **Gentian** is the mildest depression of the group. All of them are serious, of course.

Lately, SWEETIE is too worried about pork futures
to even eat her CHESTNUTS.

VERVAIN
Hyperactive; Intense

WHAT IT'S NEEDED FOR:

No relaxation for these intense, hard driving work-a-holics who are always committed to some project, cause or injustice.

They are very focused on their current burning desire and use their vast energies to mobilize everyone to go in their direction. It is the only way to go, of course, and they can become volatile, even violent, with those who get in their way or disagree.

There is only black/white, right/-wrong in their book and they give 150% of themselves to convince the world. Their mouths are usually moving and they tire others.

In the negative, they are the fanatics of the world, even passionate revolutionaries who will use terrorism to gain their ends.

Preachers at heart, the more benign **Vervains** will always find a soapbox and are willing to face ridicule to defend principles. They are always "on call" and can't rest until everyone understands the urgency of the situation.

Such high-strung stress and tension can leave the immune system worn out and illnesses develop.

Parents can be **Vervains** in their determinations for their children who are given little to say about their own lives.

THE RESULTS ARE:

Many of the wrongs of the world have been righted by positive **Vervains** who calmly and wisely inspire others to noble causes. They are skilled diplomats who let others talk in order to build bridges of understanding.

They may even review their own position as they develop more patience and tolerance. They look at situations in a wider context and realize that truth does not need hard sell.

The **Vervain** plant is a robust, upright perennial . . . very like a person in the positive. With a Divine unrest, they strive to help the underdogs of the world. At the same time, they nourish, exercise and relax the body that is to be the torch bearer for justice.

They are courageous and willing to face danger, possibly even prison or death, as they work with missionary zeal. However, they are now more optimistic and realize God's time is not theirs.

Most are not called to be Joan of Arc, or even Ralph Nader, but even God seemed to want a **Vervain** on His side as He knocked St. Paul off his horse.

The activist, the volunteer, the parent all can inspire others with love, understanding and enthusiasm as their lives get into perspective.

* * *

Definitely, a personality Remedy.

First, get the elephant off your own foot.

VINE
Dominating; Enjoys Power

WHAT IT'S NEEDED FOR:

"Do it my way!" is the **Vine** refrain as they ride roughshod over those under them. This can be a political, family or workplace dictator.

These out-of-balance leaders know their own abilities and crave power. They often rule with fear and seldom argue . . . after all, they're right.

These are the ruthless tyrants of history who cruelly stopped at nothing to gain their own egotistical ends. But many **Vines** can also be found in the workplace who have no consideration for the feelings, opinions or ideas of subordinates.

One worker daily misted the office of her boss with **Vine**. She should also have taken it to protect herself from this volcanic force.

Domestic tyrants may be under dominating superiors at work to cause them to be so abusive and hard. Greedy for power, they can cause lifelong scars and, perhaps, be creating a school bully. There can be a trickle down situation.

Long known in the military, **Vines** can also be found in volunteer organizations, the pulpit and all levels of supervisorship.

Can also need **Chicory**.

THE RESULTS ARE:

Gentle leaders who are great in a crisis and who can motivate instead of push. They direct with confidence but respect others and are fair with them.

By showing appreciation, they can inspire others to aspire beyond what they previously felt they could do.

They are survivors who can always be counted on to find a way for all when there is a problem.

With **Vine** they are less aggressive, but have a natural authority which they can use to encourage teamwork. This can be at home, the workplace or in organizations.

Vine can also encourage leaders to develop. Although quick thinkers and capable, they may have some weaknesses which need to be overcome, i.e., **Mimulus** for fears; **Larch** for self-doubt; **Pine** for guilt, etc.

All leaders have some anxieties and tension which can cause them physical problems and pain. Inflexibility can cause high blood pressure, headaches, digestive and other problems. **Vine** can dissipate these as they learn to use their powerful energy to guide others as a wise, loving teacher and good shepherd.

Now Jane, watch your grip!
You're a little too far over . . . etc., etc.

WALNUT
Transition Periods of Life

WHAT IT'S NEEDED FOR:

Although **Walnut** was meant to prevent undue influences on those aiming for their own life's goal, it has proven helpful for all the changes of life.

Give for: teething babies, puberty, pregnancy, change of life (male or female), retirement, changes required after a major illness, terminal stage of life. A peaceful transition can be made through all biological changes.

It is a release from pain of moving, leaving old friends, fellow employees, separating couples, divorce, death of someone close (including pets).

Walnut protects from dominating, forceful personalities, the pressure of unwanted circumstances, the hinderances of those keeping a person from his/her chosen path.

Along with **Rescue** and **Chicory**, we use **Walnut** for people wishing to separate from addictions of overeating, nicotine, caffeine, sugar, alcohol, tranquilizers, etc. It helps to keep them from falling back into old habits. **Chestnut Bud** also keeps them determined.

When trying to take great steps forward, it is a link breaker from old thoughts, associations, influences. Also, changing professions, religions, locations, jobs, schools, etc.

THE RESULTS ARE:

The constancy and determination to carry out beliefs, life's work, ambitions without being affected by strong opinions and personalities; even ridicule for mental and/or spiritual new beginnings.

Dr. Bach was a true **Walnut,** leaving social approval, financial security and all his medical and professional training behind to seek a new way that he believed in. He persevered against all advice, lack of encouragement and peer pressures.

Many **Walnuts** are ahead of their time as innovators, explorers, inventors and, yes, even the unconventional.

Stable people, unaffected by vital inner or outer changes.

Very helpful as a screen of protection against illnesses or negative emotions of those required to be in close contact with people: doctors, dentists, nurses, massage and physical therapists.

If there are physical sufferings because of still remembering the past . . . and possible regrets, **Honeysuckle** may be added.

Completely free in spirit, they can follow their own inner guidance and progress toward fulfilling their life's mission without deviating.

Goodbye, WALLY!

WATER VIOLET
Proud; Uninvolved with Others

WHAT IT'S NEEDED FOR:

A quiet, reserved person who has an invisible barrier around him/-her. Doesn't want interference, even when ill, and doesn't want to be involved in the lives of others.

Because they often seem conceited and aloof, they are frequently lonely and disappointed.

The "stiff upper lip" mentality does not allow them to discuss emotions, much less feel them. They prefer to talk about intellectual matters or even current events.

They can't express grief or love. Their frozen personality does not allow an "I love you."

Quite intelligent usually, they may feel superior, even disdainful, to others. Pride can cause a tenseness and stiffness, a mental rigidity, which results in physical and emotional problems.

Can be helpful for lonely widows, widowers or others who find it difficult to venture out of their shell.

For those who feel isolated after moving, especially children and teens who miss friends and familiar faces.

Water Violets can become impatient (**Impatiens**) as they "do not suffer fools gladly." Rarely would they also be a pushy **Vine**.

THE RESULTS ARE:

Islands of peace, they are charming and approachable. Others frequently ask their advice.

Because they have poise and inner dignity, they can set inspiring examples as teachers, parents, therapists, healers.

They have great individuality (not happy for long in a rut) and are free from the influence and opinions of others.

As they open up and share themselves, they can have much more joy and happiness. Others are attracted to them.

They make excellent supervisors because they are conscientious, practical, capable and above the petty problems of those around them.

From keeping emotions pent up for so long, there can be a "healing crisis" with tears and an outpouring of grief. Especially for reserved men, this can be a very painful period.

By sticking with **Water Violet** for some weeks, however, the result will be a richer personality who is able to feel and love . . . and express feelings. The positive **Water Violet** can now share not only knowledge but self.

VIOLET'S very reliable and smart
but she doesn't mix with others too well.

WHITE CHESTNUT
Mind Spinning With Unwanted Thoughts

WHAT IT'S NEEDED FOR:

Deep fatigue can result from worries racing around and around in our minds like a hamster on a wheel.

If this happens in the daytime, a person can have difficulty concentrating and their work suffers. Even worse, they can be so preoccupied that they have an accident.

At night they may be helpless to prevent their thoughts from going over the same matters again and again. As they toss in bed, trying to escape from their own thoughts, they solve nothing.

If there has been a disagreement, the arguments and counter-arguments may be what causes the persistent thoughts.

There are two Remedies for insominia . . . this is one. The other is **Agrimony** if a person is keeping problems to him/herself and outwardly appearing very cheerful. At times both remedies may be needed as this tiredness can result in depression and irritability.

Hornbeam, great for fatigue, may be requested by a person but it is important to find the cause. It is often a need for **White Chestnut** and/or **Agrimony.**

THE RESULTS ARE:

Peace and rest finally come as the mind is restored to calm and quiet.

The mental chatter ceases and, suddenly, solutions become obvious. Of course, if the problem is that the person is going to stay up late to watch horror movies or the late news on TV (the same thing), the solution may not be Remedies.

Often, the problem is that a person cannot leave their work at their place of business (mentally or, actually, in a briefcase). **White Chestnut** can be most helpful. So is physical exercise and getting other interests to think about.

Some people keep a bottle of **Rescue** plus **White Chestnut** beside their bed in case they wake in the middle of the night and can't get back to sleep. Some health practitioners say that waking between 3 and 5 a.m. indicates a gall bladder and/or liver that needs cleaning out. We can't confirm that but water and lemon juice is helpful anyway.

We have powerful minds that need to stay balanced and tranquil so that they can be put to constructive uses, undisturbed by outside influences. We also need to "not cross bridges before we come to them."

Helpful for meditation.

I'm getting that Deja Vu feeling again.

WILD OAT
Seeking a Purpose in Life

WHAT IT'S NEEDED FOR:

Dissatisfied with present situation but doesn't know which direction to go in. May be frustrated, bored, feeling unfulfilled.

Ambitious and unusually bright and talented and wants to do something important with their lives . . . but what?

Is interested in many things but doesn't know where to fit in; difficult to make a commitment.

May have started many things; even many professions (and **was** formerly interested) but now has creative unrest. May even find associates boring. And life is passing by. "What is my true vocation?"

This could be a mid-life crisis. Possibly parents didn't allow the person to make own decisions. May overeat; have sexual problems.

A student being pushed to decide on a career or major. A retiree searching for purposefulness in life. Regrets.

Always looking, reaching but never getting to a satisfying goal. Can be depressed . . . or have energies going in all directions.

THE RESULTS ARE:

Finds life's path; knows what they want to do in life. Has PEACE. Can judge by health and happiness if this is all so.

Gifted; achieves easily; has definite ambitions. Finds the experiences of life interesting and challenging.

Calmer, clearer, more certain. Knows their talents are needed for others and this is where the real satisfaction lies.

More fulfilled. Not running off in all directions. Keeps many interests but defines profession(s), hobbies and those thing there isn't much time for.

They are never sheep but "Master of all they survey." May find new friends, peers because they may have been with some not up to their level of ability or ambition. May still not fit in with society as a whole but isn't disturbed by being "different." Water seeks its own level. They will attract the right ones who can help them and they can help.

Vocational and life decisions are made. If there is a choice between only two situations, **Scleranthus** can also help.

Accepts guidance of Higher Self and lets go of self-will and self-centeredness. May develop intuition.

* * *

Wild Oat and **Holly** are suggested if too many different Bach Remedies seem to be called for.

He may look like WILD OATS
but at least he seems to have a goal in life.

WILD ROSE
Passive; Bored; Apathetic

WHAT IT'S NEEDED FOR:

A dull, expressionless voice may distinguish the fatalistic or bored **Wild Rose** type.

The drifters of life, they are more sad than depressed. Life just isn't worth living for them but they are resigned to take whatever comes their way.

This can be from an unhappy home life, intense constant work, no-zip long-term relationships, a miscarriage or death of a close one.

"Well, that's the way it is. I can't do anything about it," might be a typical remark.

In illness, a person may not be very cooperative because "nothing will help." May have been given an incurable verdict or a "Sorry, there is nothing more we can do." May feel a condition is hereditary and accepts this with resignation.

Bored school children; "I don't care" teens and even passive babies may need **Wild Rose.** External circumstances may not seem to warrant this condition for young ones or adults.

Half dead, tired vegetables of life, they may not complain . . . why bother. Empty, indifferent people, others may find them boring and tiresome.

THE RESULTS ARE:

The big and little pleasures of life now bring joy and happiness. They now become interested in many things.

They understand that they may have created some of their own circumstances and have the power to alter or eliminate conditions in their lives.

They may be suffering from burn-out or long term unemployment, but **Wild Rose** will gradually bring inner motivation and "put a tiger in their tank."

As enthusiasm returns, they cope with life better and others find them more interesting. They may find that, as their spirits revive, they become involved in sports, various activities and even daily decisions they previously ignored.

No longer constantly tired, they are able to plunge into life with joyful expectancy and spontaneity. Yes! Things can be different! A positive attitude can make it so.

This is not an easy condition to change because vibrations must be brought up so far. It may take a long term commitment. Helpful to add **Holly,** the highest vibrational Remedy, because it floods the soul with love.

WILLOW
Resentment; Disappointment

WHAT IT'S NEEDED FOR:

The cards of life seem to be stacked against the **Willow** type person. They feel very sorry for themselves and can be quite cynical.

They resent strongly . . . perhaps family member(s), friends, neighbors, work associates. They may have a grudge that has gone on for years. They won't usually confront the person(s) they are so angry at and get it settled. They are more like smouldering volcanos and they poison the atmosphere and themselves with their blanket of negativity.

They have a victim complex and feel the world owes them. They are not grateful for anything done for them and are stingy and ungiving themselves.

They may have powerful prejudices against a family, a neighborhood, a town, a race, creed, color or country. Sarcastic Archie Bunkers, their personal sun is blotted out more with each grumbling, spiteful thought.

If recovering, they don't like to admit it. As a patient, nothing pleases or satisfies them. They may seem much older than they are.

THE RESULTS ARE:

They become master of their own thoughts and realize they can attract unpleasant circumstances or happy situations.

Our thoughts may be all we can control at times but we need to guard them continuously. Most of us at times have some moody, angry thoughts that we direct at the world. They can become chronic if we don't become aware that we are responsible for what we think.

Everyone suffers disappointments and setbacks in life but to blame the circumstances and never look at ourselves (as **Willow** helps us to do), is not to realize we are architects of our own destiny.

As **Willow** engenders a return of optimism and faith in our fellowman, the formerly alienated becomes friendlier and more youthful looking. Possibly illnesses like arthritis and headaches dissolve.

Looking at life in perspective, we can laugh at our misfortunes as the latest learning experience. A sense of humor replaces the "wet blanket" and everyone enjoys it a lot more.

Instead of begrudging the happiness or good luck of others, there is now rejoicing.

I know it's not fair that he was promoted first
but the boss has problems too, you know.

RESCUE

Remember the five Remedies
in Rescue by thinking of:

CIRCUS

C   **Clematis**

I   **Impatiens**

R   **Rock Rose**

CU   **Cherry Plum**

S   **Star of Bethlehem**

RESCUE
For Big and Small Emergencies

It was a night of raging storm along the Norfolk coast of England. The winds blew and howled and the waters violently churned. For anyone caught at sea, it was a time of panic and despair.

Two men, caught on a tile barge, fought the elements as long as they could and desperately tried for shore. It was no use. They were tossed back by the capricious, foaming sea. At last, exhausted and without hope, they lashed themselves to the mast so they wouldn't be swept overboard.

Hours later, the rage was spent and a lifeboat crew from the fishing village of Cromer spotted the helpless barge and went after it.

The two seemingly lifeless forms were lifted into the lifeboat, their clothes stiff from the salt spray. As the craft made for shore, the townspeople began to gather and one shouted, "Get Dr. Bach."

The year was 1930 and Edward Bach, M.D. had made Cromer his home for much of the year since leaving his London medical practice. Usually he was walking through the fields, looking for more wild flowers which would heal the emotions and problems of people. The weather had been too bad, however, and now he came running to help in any way he could.

He always carried a small bottle of his herbal "remedies" that had proven helpful in emergencies. Now, as the two men were brought ashore, Dr. Bach could see that the younger one was blue in the face, almost frozen and seemed beyond hope. He dashed into the water and began to apply his drops to the lips of the unconscious man.

As the men made their way up the beach toward a nearby house, the doctor continued to frequently apply the drops. Soon, the sailor opened his eyes and color began to return to his face. At this point, Dr. Bach put the drops directly into his mouth. Within a few minutes he sat up, looked clear-eyed and asked, "Has anyone got a cigarette?" He made a full recovery within a couple days.

The amazed villagers called it a real rescue for Dr. Bach, and **Rescue** became the name of the combination. At that time, there were three different flowers in the Remedy and, later, two more were added.

THE FIVE REMEDIES

Although it is sometimes called the 39th **Remedy, Rescue** is simply a combination of five other Remedies. They are:

Clematis, for the spacy, befuddled mind which seems jammed in a trauma. Also, for unconsciousness, fainting. It helps with the clear thinking needed in an emergency.

Impatiens for the pain, impatience or nervousness which can accompany mental stress and tension. It helps calm a person.

Rock Rose is for terror, panic or any great fear which comes with an upset . . . or even looking forward to a stressful situation.

Cherry Plum is for any desperate feelings or fear of losing mental or physical control. Under stress some people can have coughing or sneezing attacks or are even not able to control their bladder. Others become rigid and unable to function, as in shock. Still others become hysterical and out of control.

Star of Bethlehem may be the most important as it neutralizes the effects of trauma so that it can't remain at the cellular level, mentally or physically.

Rescue is non-toxic, non-habit forming and without side effects. Despite its life saving potential, it should not be considered a panacea for everything or a substitute for qualified medical assistance when needed. However, since the body in shock cannot start to heal itself, it can be a stabilizing treatment until personnel from 9-1-1 arrive or a person gets to a doctor.

These five Remedies work synergistically. That is, they are like strands of a rope, when intertwined they are much stronger than when used individually.

It is hoped that eventually clinical studies will prove the effectiveness of **Rescue** but, until then, we only have thousands of success stories to go on. Also, it costs millions of dollars for a scientific study and there is no money for one. Dr. Bach wanted to keep his Remedies reasonable and available to everyone. This precludes anyone, such as drug companies, making a great deal of money from them as they would a drug. Therefore, no studies.

If a person faints, or is unconscious, the drops can be applied to the lips, the gums, the wrists, behind the ears or to the back of the neck. We have also used this method if someone was sobbing or hysterical and it was not possible to get them to take the drops internally. Or, if someone doesn't know what **Rescue** is, and is unwilling to take it, they will usually let you touch their wrists.

RESCUE CREAM

There is also a **Rescue** Cream that can be used externally. Mothers find this very helpful for children who are always getting bumped, bruised or frightened. The drops they find useful for themselves as they try to cope with the day's emergencies.

Prepared in a homeopathic, non-allergenic cream base, it can be successfully used for sprains, minor burns, insect bites, scratches and even hemorrhoids. Some also use the cream for muscle tightness or pain. It can be applied to a gauze and bandaged over wounds or an affected area.

OTHER USES FOR RESCUE

Rescue is wonderful for great sorrow. I always bring a bottle when attending a funeral if I think there are those likely to use it. Many tell us how much it helped them get through a difficult situation without falling apart. They still have the grief and the problem but they are able to handle it with calm and clarity.

Even happy occasions can make a person (group) nervous. It is delightful for weddings, showers, proms, retirement parties or any large gathering where people are expected to look and act just right. I wish I'd had it for the young man who locked himself out of his car after he arrived to pick up my daughter for their prom.

There are everyday scrapes, headaches, smashed fingers or toes or near accidents for which **Rescue** is a blessing. Some use it before a speaking engagement, job interview, taking an exam or going to talk to someone about a subject they would rather avoid.

After any argument, before making a hospital visit or going to a courtroom, it can restore calm and confidence.

Some psychologists, hypno-therapists, and even a few enlightened psychiatrists, use it routinely. Other therapists find it to be of great occasional help as do some doctors, dentists, chiropractors and other professionals. I once gave some **Rescue** to a dentist to use on his patients. I had used it before seeing him. Later, I discovered he was taking it himself when he had a particularly difficult patient or job to perform.

RESCUE WITH CRAB APPLE
IS GREAT FOR THE EYES.
It makes a soothing eye wash and is very helpful
for eyes itching and burning from allergies.

Rescue is often used for insomnia. For minds also going around and around with mental chatter or arguments, add **White Chestnut** to the formula. Of course, it might not totally overcome the effects of a late night horror show. We would like to see Rescue used sensibly and not as a routine life saver for someone whose lifestyle is lacking in common sense.

Results with children using Remedies of any kind are often quicker than when used with adults. **Rescue** is wonderful if they have nightmares, stomach aches (try to discover the source), falls, frights and all the other things that seem to happen to young ones. They soon learn to ask for the "magic drops."

Normally, four drops are taken by mouth and held under the tongue for a minute, or put into a small glass of water and sipped. When a wasp stung me, I applied **Rescue** externally and then took some by mouth. Then, I got a wide-mouthed glass, put four drops in with some water and stuck the wounded finger in for a while. The extremely sharp pain subsided at once and, after a period of soaking, the hole closed up and no pain remained. Later in the day, the finger had a slight sensation when I rubbed it, but no pain.

For small animals, use four drops of **Rescue** in their water if they are having a problem. Use 10 drops per bucket for large animals. They will mellow almost instantly.

Drooping, unhappy plants will also respond if you put 10 drops in a gallon of water (or, proportionately, if smaller amount is needed). They often perk right up. Someone loves them.

A person can also put **Rescue** in the bath water, use it as a compress or mist a room with it. It works amazingly on all living things.

Instruments of Grace
To Help Us Perfect Ourselves

1. It is a very simple system . . . IF you are not thinking and analyzing it a whole lot. Get in touch with your inner Self.

2. Every caring, compassionate individual can work with the Remedies with good results. It is not dependent on educational level.

3. Your part is a very humble one . . . simply serve as an agent of helpfulness.

4. It is a very uplifting system for receiver and practitioner.

5. They work on a vibrational level but the more you work with them, the less you may understand how they work. And that's OK.

6. Bach Remedies can be used with reliability on **all** living things including plants and animals.

7. The remedies can be used with **ALL** other systems of healing. They will not interfere . . . only enhance.

8. The life force from the flowers is constant . . . it is not necessary to add or subtract.

9. Helping people, working with the Remedies should be fun and bring a sense of joy.

10. At times the Remedies put you in touch with some difficult emotions. They will increase your inner strength so you can deal with problems/challenges and learn what lesson is being taught to you.

11. Nature has provided gifts which cannot be tarnished but only help us to grow in understanding that we are all one with the ONE.

"Color healing and Bach Flower Remedies will be the healing methods of the future."   --Dr. Bernard Jensen

As therapists we must see the potential in all others. We must not put limitations on anyone. By our being happy and hopeful, others are encouraged. They can go beyond our expectations if we don't limit them. Listen to the client, but rely on what is in you that is greater for guidance.

AGRIMONY:
Crying on the Inside

"How are you?" you ask.

"Oh, fantastic! Couldn't be better, " comes the reply.

Your friend has either just been listening to Zig Zigler tapes or is one of those rare balanced individuals who has succeeded in improving their holistic life so that they are full of love, light and mental, physical and spiritual health.

On the other hand, they could be an Agrimony. That's the Bach Flower Remedy for a person who is jovial, fun to be with and seems to be on top of the world. Inside they are miserable, torn up and crying for help. But they'll never let you know.

Insomnia is a frequent visitor for the Agrimony type as this tortured soul cannot find peace even in sleep. If the mind is going around and around with mental arguments that cannot be silenced even for the night, **White Chestnut** can also be of great value.

When brought into the positive, an Agrimony type is a genuine optimist. They can look at problems as "challenges" and "opportunities" and lessons that must be learned if looked at in the right perspective.

They'll make jokes about their pains and discomforts as they don't consider them important in the greater scheme of life. They are true peace lovers and do not want to distress anyone with worrying about any of their problems.

Agrimony types don't easily share their inner selves . . . their deep feelings and emotions. They can't allow people into their space to share their hurt. Sometimes, those who love them feel shut out. However, "pain shared is pain relieved," is not part of their personal philosophy.

They love to be with people and talk about business, sports, the news, fashions or whatever interests them. Many find discussions about religion, metaphysics or politics too close to personal feelings unless they know they are with someone who shares their views.

If a Bach Flower practitioner finds a person is an Agrimony type . . . and is in the negative . . . there will be immediate concern because this individual can easily resort to drugs or alcohol to ease the pain. While they might make a great party person or drinking companion, they can be doing serious harm to their health. Studies now prove these negative emotions can cause a great many organic illnesses. Digestion problems, ulcers, stomach and gall bladder illnesses are just a few of the possible disorders that can result. Skin eruptions, including psoriasis, can cause great discomfort as can constipation and other bowel problems.

Agrimony tends to be a personality type and so a person cannot get rid of this characteristic . . . and shouldn't try. They are

It's hard to believe AGGIE just lost his job, needs a gall bladder operation and has the tax people after him.

delightful people to have around. But it is vital that they stay in the positive . . . and be aware of the great personal harm they can do to themselves in the negative.

Agrimony is a fairly common trait and during the Olympics in Korea it was discovered that there was nearly a whole country of people with this characteristic as part of their culture.

Newsweek magazine wrote . . . "the head of the complaint department, Young Kim, wrestled with the notion that his people are culturally adverse to acknowledging that complaints even exist. A Korean would rather put on a big smile and say. 'We'll try to get it done,' knowing full well he can't, Young said. 'It's ingrained in our culture to avoid that perceived unpleasantness.' "

When we asked a local Korean lady about this, she agreed. "Even in close family relationships we don't want to distress anyone, so we don't admit anything is wrong. If my mother asked about my husband or our marriage, I would never admit to there being a problem. It might upset her."

And the result of keeping all these problems inside? The Korean lady said there was a lot of alcoholism in her country, particularly among men.

While there are many exceptions, men do have trouble expressing their feelings more than women. One doctor has suggested that this is why they die younger.

Bach Flower Remedies can be very helpful in dealing with this problem of internal anguish. It is not explainable but it often brings some enlightenment to a person so that they can mentally sort out and solve their concerns.

The main reason for the failure of modern medical science is that it is dealing with results not causes . . .
. . . disease in its origin is not material . . .
Disease is in essence the result of conflict between Soul and Mind, and will never be eradicated except by spiritual and mental effort.

--Edward Bach M.D. in *Heal Thyself*

ALL DAY LONG . . .
Beech, Beech, Beech!

Being positive enough to always see the good in others is a wonderful trait. Unfortunately, most of us don't make it a lot of the time. That's when we need to take some of Dr. Bach's **Beech** drops.

Maybe lots for the "picky-picky" person who drives us all a little into the negative. Visit their house and make sure you take your shoes off at the door; don't move a pillow or magazine out of place and it's to die if you should spill something.

This is known to Bach practitioners as a **Beech** personality. The male **Beech** has every tool in place and you can nearly eat off his garage floor. They are not only fussy about themselves (they dress meticulously, of course), but they are very aware of *your* haircut, clothes, car, etc. And they happily let you know of imperfections.

Now, admittedly, there are parents who would give up a year of pizza to have their kids resemble the neatness description. We understand. We have lived in a house where our offspring's bedroom needed to be fumigated and sealed from the public.

Since the function of the Remedies is to restore balance, we would also feel that **Beech** is good for these children. Besides, they usually complain a lot about everything . . . school, your rules and, of course, anything resembling healthy food. "Yuk! What's that green stuff?"

We would probably also add some **Wild Rose** to their bottle of remedies. This wonderful plant gives us an essence which is good for apathy, no inclination to make an effort or a drifter on the sea of life.

Bach Remedies are not true homeopathy, but they work on some of the same principles and only a minute amount is required to obtain seeming miracles. Dr. Bach was never concerned with specific diseases; only with the mental and emotional state of his patients. By a vibrational means, the remedies help a person into a positive state of mind and it is like turning on a light in a dark room. When there is light, there can be no darkness. It acts very subtly, but effectively. Physical problems start to melt away when a person is mentally, emotionally and spiritually balanced.

People constantly ask what Remedy to take for a certain disease but it is always the individual who must be considered. It's true a perfectionist or **Beech** personality could be rigid enough to get arthritis, or even M.S., but it also might manifest as headaches or digestion problems.

The **Beech** person has an intolerance for the faults of others and can become very upset by small habits or mannerisms. "Don't pick your nose in public!" may be good parental training but if it is done by a person who nags about everything, **Beech** is needed.

Dr. Bach wrote about **Beech** being "For those who feel the need to see more good and beauty in all that surrounds them. And, although much appears to be wrong, they have the ability to see the good growing within. So as to be able to be more tolerant, lenient and understanding of the different way each individual and all things are working to their own final perfection."

In the positive, **Beech** people have strong beliefs but always look for the good in others. They try to be more sympathetic and understanding of shortcomings. Dr. Bach's view of a perfect example of tolerance was Jesus being crucified but asking for forgiveness for those responsible.

There might be special times when you feel **Beech** would help you stay "cool." For instance, if you are going to visit (or receive a visit) from someone who really irritates you, it would help. Some people feel they need it if they are going to be around someone's annoying children.

Outside things can bother a person to the extreme also . . . noises, pollens, barking dogs, travel complications, weather conditions or even certain foods. So, "Don't sweat the small stuff." If you are intolerant of anything, try some **Beech** Remedy.

HONEYSUCKLE
Living In The Past

Psychologists tell us there is a tendency to remember good from the past, while the bad becomes fuzzy and less important. Studies also show that the elderly can often be helped by encouraging them to talk about the past and relive their memories.

The flip side of this can be the damage done to anyone who constantly lives in the past. This may be "homesickness" or a feeling of aloneness because family and/or friends have moved or died. Perhaps a "significant other" is no longer around.

People in this state can become so engrossed in the past that vital forces slow down and they cannot be productive in the NOW.

A desire to bring back the good old days was typified in the popular song,

"Those were the days my friend;
We thought they'd never end."

Dr. Bach probably spent some time living in the past and realized that, because of it, his energy and productivity levels were down. Being a high achiever in his search for a simple way to cure the ills of man, he no doubt started walking over the English countryside. A flower that would heal this state of mind, and the physical problems that could follow, was found in the beautiful **Honeysuckle.**

This Remedy is not just for the elderly. It might be for a salesman or business person who can only recall their BIG deal and how great the successful feeling was. Present productivity suffers.

Reliving the past can also bring regrets. **Honeysuckle** can help forgive the past. It is gone. There is only now.

It is good to enjoy some nostalgia, unless it takes away the ability to grow and deal with the present. We need that.

Are you agonizing over all your ambitions that did not happen? **Wild Oats** can help you with new goals. **Honeysuckle** can bring the Bluebird of Happiness as you shift gears into being aware of all the new opportunities which await you.

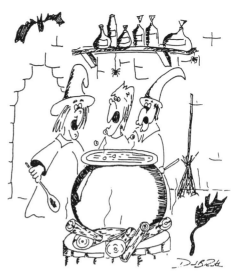

Oh, HONEY, remember the good ol' days before the government outlawed Eye of Newt and SUCKLING Dragon's Scales?

From Dr. Bach's "Free Thyself"

There are great qualities in which all men are gradually perfecting themselves, possibly concentrating upon one or two at a time. They are...

Love	Gentleness	Wisdom
Sympathy	Strength	Forgiveness
Peace	Understanding	Courage
Steadfastness	Tolerance	Joy

And it is by perfecting these qualities in ourselves that each one of us is raising the whole world a step nearer to its final unthinkably glorious goal. . . . we are seeking no selfish gain of personal merit, but that every single human being . . . is of the same importance in the Divine Plan, and is given the same mighty privilege of being a saviour of the world simply by knowing that he is a perfect child of the Creator.

. . . so there are hindrances, or interferences . . . These are the real causes of disease:

Restraint	Indifference	Ignorance
Fear	Weakness	Impatience
Restlessness	Doubt	Terror
Indecision	Over-enthusiasm	Grief

These, if we allow them, will reflect themselves in the body - causing what we call disease. Not understanding the real causes, we have attributed disharmony to external influences, germs, cold, heat and have given names to the results, arthritis, cancer, asthma, etc.: thinking that disease begins in the physical body.

. . . Real health is happiness .... health is there for us to accept any time we like.

— From **The Original Writings of Edward Bach,** pp. 46-47.

PINE
If You Can Never Do Enough

Will you stop saying, "I'm sorry!" you feel like saying to some people. They are constantly apologizing, even if it isn't their fault.

This is the guilt-ridden personality who always feels a need to do better. Often this is a very bright, successful person who frequently overworks but is never content with achievements.

This type has set such high standards that emotional stress is common. Because of never being content, they may have trouble sleeping and this results in always feeling tired and depressed. They have little joy in life even though they usually do things well.

Dr. Bach discovered a Remedy for these over-conscientious sufferers in the flowers of the PINE tree. As with the other 38 Bach Remedies, PINE is most effective when taking four drops, four times a day, alone or in a formula.

After taking the Remedy for a while, a person will start to "hang loose" a little more and have a more balanced attitude about self. He/she may still be willing to take on many responsibilities but will no longer be an uncomplaining scapegoat or ashamed of errors.

The feeling of not being good enough will give way to an understanding that humanity, in the physical expression, is not a perfect creation but, as a child of God, is loved and important. This may be especially helpful if a person was raised in a rigid religion which constantly imposed guilt. Understanding a God of love, rather than of vengeance, can bring peace and happiness into a person's life.

PINE helps us to understand that our growth depends on our making some mistakes and that this helps us to love and forgive others. Everyone makes errors or "misses the mark" (the original meaning of the word "sin"). It is important to resolve to try and do better but to let go all feelings of guilt. What we did was in the past . . . it no longer exists. We are divinely forgiven; now we must forgive ourselves.

PINE can be most helpful when working with abused children (who somehow feel they must deserve such treatment) or assisting the "child within" us to recover. It can also be useful when there was a death of a loved one and there is a feeling that something more should have been done.

Sometimes **PINE** is used to set new goals by a person who has been expecting too much of self. With affirmations such as, "I accept myself as I am," a person can go a long way toward being more relaxed and, possibly, avoid illnesses which could be brought on by constant stress.

Guilt feelings can even make people accident-prone as they subconsciously punish themselves for their faults. Even in illness **PINE** types may apologize . . . for the things they can't get done or because they should somehow have prevented the illness.

Dr Bach wrote, "No great ascent was ever made without faults and falls, and they must be regarded as experiences which will help us to stumble less in the future. . . . We need to realize that one trace of condemnation against ourselves, or others, is a trace of condemnation against the Universal Creation of Love, and restricts us, limits our power to allow the Universal Love to flow through us to others."

This is why, after taking **PINE**, a person may experience more energy as Divine Love is allowed to flow through the soul. Forgiveness is the key to happiness and it starts with forgiveness of self.

129

WALNUT
Is For Life's Changes

"We're moving AGAIN. Get out the Walnut. And don't forget to give some to the cat. Kitty has trouble changing too."

"Walnut" is the Bach Flower Remedy that is used for all the changes in our lives. And these days are times of change . . . physically, mentally and/or spiritually for most of us. We may even be breaking away from old ideas or a dominating personality in our life.

Of all the things humans have the most difficulty with, change usually leads the list. We like our comfort zone . . . no matter how bad it is . . . and moving out of it is sometimes very frustrating. In fact, we might get very stressed over it.

We may be oversensitive to certain influences and realize we need to break away. Sometimes, we find that even good friends are no longer in our line of thinking as we have worked to grow and expand our consciousness. Links with the past are the hardest to break and, when we see that our course in life is being hampered, it becomes painful to make the change.

We are always having some kind of change in life from teething to puberty to menopause to being a senior citizen. Each time of change may have its own challenges. **Walnut** can be a gentle, soothing help. **Aspen** may be added to the bottle of remedies also as this is for apprehension, or not being sure or secure in our feelings.

The apprehension might come from changing jobs, moving or even deciding to break a personal link with someone for whom there is an attachment. If the change is very traumatic, such as in a divorce, **Star of Bethlehem** might be added to the formula.

What happens when you take the **Walnut** and other remedies? It is like turning on a light in a dark room. The negative, fearful feelings just vanish and a positive, optimistic outlook develops.

There is a determination to carry out whatever needs to be done in spite of problems that arise or even other's opinions or ridicule.

If a person is considering a big decision, they might want to add **Scleranthus** to the formula which helps when trying to make up a mind which says "yes" and then "no" about a particular change.

For some people, change is an everyday happening and they float through it without distress. For instance, if you are married to a builder, the question is sometimes, "The walls are getting dirty. Should we wash, paint or move?" You move. **Walnut** is helpful, but perhaps not needed as much as for someone who has not moved for 20 or more years.

The personality of the individual is always considered when discussing which Remedies would be best . . . everyone is different and reacts in different ways. The drops are totally harmless if they are given to someone who doesn't need them. But, for those who need them, they can be a wonderful blessing.

Goodbye, WALLY!!

STAR OF BETHLEHEM
For the Shocks and Traumas of Life

Of the 38 Flower Remedies that Dr. Bach discovered to help our various emotional problems, none is more valued than **Star of Bethlehem**. The essence of this dainty flower has the power to neutralize the shocks, fears and traumas of life. Dr. Bach called it "the comforter and soother of pains and sorrows."

Many consider it the most important Remedy in **Rescue**, that invaluable combination of five Remedies, which has helped so many thousands (or millions) recover from any type of upset. Working synergistically with the other four Remedies, it neutralizes trauma so that the body can start its self-healing process.

If the trauma is not dissipated, it can remain at the cellular and subconscious level for many years. For instance, because of a boating accident in which a person nearly drowned as a child, there may remain a morbid fear of water for the rest of that person's life.

That is why, if other Remedies don't seem to be working, it may be because, under a client's present problems, there is a hidden trauma so severe that it must be taken care of before any other healing can take place.

Because of this, many people take **Star of Bethlehem** as part of their formula, the first time they use Remedies. After the first bottle is gone, it is possible to take **Star** out of the formula . . . unless there has been some severe trauma since the first bottle was formulated.

Dr. Bach did not mean the Remedies to be the only form of cure but understood that ALL healing must ultimately come from within.

About **Star** he wrote: "**For those in great distress under conditions which, for a time, produce great unhappiness. The shock of serious news, the loss of someone dear, the fright following an accident, and such like. For those who, for a time, refuse to be consoled, this Remedy brings comfort.**"

Star is related to the onion and garlic and one florist described it as very hardy. He said that **Star of Bethlehem** surprises everyone because it lasts longer than any other cut flower.

We are not sure if this strength is the reason it is so powerful, but it no doubt has a **powerful** job to do and many have testified to its great help.

Sometimes there is a delayed reaction to a serious disappointment or shock from fear, grief or an accident. When this is realized, **Star of Bethlehem** should be taken alone or in a formula with about three other Remedies. Many have found that the Remedies seem to work best when there are only four, or possibly five, Remedies in a formula.

As the Remedies touch the soul and bring it into a positive frame, mental and/or physical problems begin to melt away and life can be put into perspective. A complete sense of well-being returns as spiritual sunlight floods mind and soul and negative feelings no longer remain.

I know it was awesome, but
you must also admit it was traumatic

(Editor's note: Since <u>Blossoms of Light</u> is now out of print and there are some beautifully expressed thoughts in it that we have not found elsewhere, we are presenting excerpts and condensed sections. The author, Yarrow Treefriend [John R. Stowe], has graciously consented to this for which we thank him.)

Blossoms of Light

In this time of planetary transformation, there is a large scale spiritual awakening which is our hope for a secure and peaceful future. We don't turn our back on technology but we redefine our relationship with nature and infuse our culture with a respect for life.

Nearly all our necessities are supplied by plants . . . food, cloth fibers, materials for shelter, fuel and herbs for medicine. We need a system of healing that can focus plant energies to change those aspects of our lives that need attention.

Flower essence therapy differs fundamentally from more familiar types of herbal medicine. In flower essences, rather than ingesting the physical herb, a person takes only its vibrational imprint that is left in the water. Flowers represent the greatest concentration of life force in the natural world. Their effects encompass the highest expression of each plant's range of properties.

Their major influences are on mental, emotional and spiritual patterns. Each essence interacts with our consciousness in a highly specific manner to stimulate our inherent powers of healing. It acts as a vibrational catalyst, a sort of tuning fork that helps us to correct a specific pattern of imbalance. Flower remedies, then, help us to cultivate positive character traits and to grow until we resonate with the highest potential we have inside.

**Flowers are a vehicle
for our personal attunement with nature.**

**Disease is a spiritual imbalance between man
and his higher guiding self.**

To work effectively with flower essences, concentrate first on getting to know their world. Intuition and attunement will eventually become major factors in your work. Be with trees and plants as much as possible. Take walks outdoors, observing with interest and respect the living beings around you. If you can, try daily meditations in a quiet, outdoor spot where you are surrounded by plants.You will be rewarded by a calm, receptive state of mind and greater attunement to the flowers. When you start to take flower remedies, your consciousness will open even more rapidly and effectively. In fact, everything will be amplified if taken outside in a natural setting.

Attitude is another factor vital to effectiveness. The respect and care with which you approach flower essences will be directly reflected in the strength of your results. Strive to remain clear and centered. Be open to guidance from your higher consciousness and keep your intent on doing the highest good.

Do not be overly attached to seeing rapid and dramatic results or you will invite disappointment. Personal transformation takes time. In time you will be greatly encouraged by the changes you observe.

Some flower essences are needed for short term use, immediate concerns. Others have larger lessons for us to learn. As one layer of imbalance is resolved, it opens to the next and the next. Healing is a continual process.

USING WITH GROUPS

Essences can be used effectively with groups. Flower remedies (would be helpful) to a couple trying to resolve conflicts and harmonize their relationship. Try a bottle of Remedies for people working together toward a specific goal, perhaps in a classroom, workshop or therapeutic situation. To strengthen prayer and study groups, prepare a mixture to promote centering and positive thinking.

We are working not only to change our individual consciousness, but also to change the collective energy of our entire species. All humankind is united on higher levels.

ANGELIC PLANT SPIRITS

For those who wish to make their own Remedies from wildflowers (not Bach Remedies), first attune to the plants you plan to use by meditating with them several times. There are a number of conscious spirit beings that are associated with each one. These include the plant devas, which are angelic beings responsible for the growth and development of all plants within a species, and a host of other spirits which range from individual fairies and elves to the overseeing devas of an entire geographical region. It is with these etheric beings that you will be working. Do not be disturbed if you cannot immediately feel their presence. Instead, be sensitive to areas of greater energy and power around each plant.

Give yourself time to attune more fully and you will eventually begin to develop greater awareness. Do not worship these beings, but treat them as respected co-workers, enlisting their cooperation to make your essences as strong as possible.

Clearly explain your procedure and ask permission to cut the flowers. Your communication will be strengthened if you form clear images, perhaps visualizing the energy of the flowers spreading through the people to surround the earth. Because your attitudes and state of mind can influence your communication, your own intentions will greatly affect the potency of your remedies. If you are sincere in your goal of promoting healing, the plant devas will respond and help you in your work.

Know that Nature spirits are gentle, loving beings. They are glad to help us if we approach them in a spirit of mutual respect and cooperation. Keep yourself open to your higher self, to the Light within you, and you have absolutely nothing to fear. Simply by being with the plants, by meditating and, most importantly, by loving them, you will experience great healing. Sensitivity takes time to develop.

In our dealings with Nature, we too often tend to look upon ourselves as separate, as somehow distinct from the rest of life. This is an illusion. We are an integral part of nature. We could not live for a week without the trees that supply our oxygen, nor the plants and animals that nourish us with their bodies.

ALL LIFE IS A CONTINUUM

In times to come, we will need all the power to heal that we can gather. The Creator invests each being, human and nonhuman alike, with specific talents. Each has a gift, a portion of itself to contribute to the stronger whole organism.

We can strive to make the human race part of one harmonious Being, so that each of us, each cell, acts in concert with all the others. Humankind cannot exist alone. Our attitudes must change. Our new spirituality must respect the role of each being within the Whole of Life. By striving for harmony, by using flower essences and other healing energies as tools given by the Creator, we will raise our awareness and effect a true revolution in consciousness. We will transform ourselves and ultimately transform our planet.

*   *   *

(Author John R. Stowe is director of EarthFriends Flower Oils; P.O. Box 8468; Atlanta, GA 30306; USA)

*   *   *

More and more we are learning about the work of the angelic plant spirits. Communicating with them seems to be a specific gift. At the Findhorn Spiritual Community in Scotland, the people were fed because some of their members were attuned to messages from the plant devas. They brought whatever material was requested and grew astonishing flowers and vegetables in soil that would normally produce nothing of value.

———

One of my students, who has an herb farm, said she became quite upset with her employees because they didn't understand "what the plants were saying."

"Just listen to them! They'll tell you what they need," she commanded. To no avail. They never heard. Finally, she has come to realize that she has a special gift and it is to be treasured and shared because many of us don't "hear." At least, not yet.

John R. Stowe

BIBLIOGRAPHY
and suggested readings

The Bach Flower Remedies including **Heal Thyself,** Dr. Edward Bach M.D.; **The Twelve Healers,** Dr. Edward Bach M.D. and **The Bach Remedies Repertory,** F.J. Wheeler, M.D.

The Bach Flower Remedies Step by Step, Judy Howard

Bach Flower Therapy, Mechthild Scheffer

The Bach Remedies, Leslie J. Kaslof

Blossoms of Light, Yarrow Treefriend (Earthfriends' John R. Stowe)

Dictionary of the Bach Flower Remedies, T.W. Hyne Jones

The Findhorn Garden, The Findhorn Community

Flower Remedies Handbook, Donna Cunningham

Flowers to the Rescue, Gregory Vlamis

Handbook of the Bach Flower Remedies, Dr. Philip M. Chancellor

Heal Your Body, Louise Hay

The Medical Discoveries of Edward Bach, Physician, Nora Weeks

New Bach Flower Body Maps, Dietmar Kramer and Helmut Wild

New Bach Flower Therapies, Dietmar Kramer

The Original Writings of Edward Bach, Judy Howard and
John Ramsell

Patterns of Life Force, Julian Barnard

Practical Uses and Applications of the Bach Flower Remedies,
Jessica Bear PhD, ND

Questions and Answers, John Ramsell

The Story of Mt. Vernon, Judy Howard

Wildflowers, Hilarion

Disease, though apparently so cruel, is in itself beneficent and for our good and, if rightly interpreted, it will guide us to our essential faults. If properly treated, it will be the cause of the removal of those faults and leave us better and greater than before. Suffering is a corrective to point out a lesson which by other means we have failed to grasp, and never can be eradicated until that lesson is learnt.

. . . those who understand and are able to read the significance of premonitory symptoms, disease may be prevented before its onset or aborted in its earlier stages if the proper corrective spiritual and mental efforts be undertaken . . . the fact that the individual is still granted physical life indicates that the Soul who rules is not without hope.

--Edward Bach M.D. in Heal Thyself

About the Author

Dr. Joyce Petrak

Born in Detroit, Michigan, Joyce Petrak was first graduated from the University of Detroit in journalism and English. A professional student, she was later certified as a high school teacher. For about 10 years, in Michigan and California, she was a photo-journalist, editor and/or teacher. Rarely is she doing just one thing. Now living south of Knoxville, Tennessee, she is married to Robert, has four adult children and two grandchildren.

Since a young age she had serious health problems . . . mostly with allergies, chronic bronchitis and upper respiratory problems. Searching for her own health, she was lead into various natural healing methods. As she improved, she began to search for reasons why she had to have been sick for over 20 years. Not liking what she discovered, and in typical **Vervain** fashion, she decided to change her profession so she could help others.

She graduated from the Michigan College of Naturopathy in 1978 as an Iridologist and Naturopathic Nutritional Consultant. In addition to seeing clients, she taught natural health classes and wrote natural living articles for local publications.

Seeing that "the ills of the body come from the ills of the mind," she began to use Bach Flower Remedies in 1980. Studies led her deeper into the mind and in February 1991 she received a doctorate in Clinical Hypnotherapy. While she incorporates all she has learned, and works with many facets of mental, physical and spiritual health, she specializes in healing the child within and spirit release therapy. After seeing over 1000 clients, she wrote "Angels, Guides & Other Spirits," about incredible events from the unseen world around us as told by a Spirit Release Therapist. Two more books are coming.